GEORGE B. MAIR

The Day Khruschev Panicked

CASSELL · LONDON

CASSELL & COMPANY LTD
35 Red Lion Square · London WC1
and at
MELBOURNE · SYDNEY · TORONTO · CAPE TOWN
JOHANNESBURG · AUCKLAND

———

380

Printed in Great Britain by
Cox & Wyman Limited, London, Fakenham and Reading
F.361

This book is dedicated to my friends Leslie and Andrew Taylor without whom life would be even more complicated than it at present is.

Contents

Introduction

WESTERN civilization almost perished between 17 and 27 September 1960, days which will be remembered by historians as marking the defeat of the most ruthless coup ever conceived by a government bent upon enslaving the world.

Events of the previous months had concealed the significance of almost everything which was going on behind the scenes, and men's thoughts centred rather upon the Congo, Fidel Castro, the Army Revolt in Turkey and key Russian technicians being flown out of China for no apparent reason.

Practically every world statesman then began to announce his intention of representing his country at United Nations and the autumn gathering of a king, princes, dictators, and presidents in New York was the only obvious clue that something serious was afoot. The slow passage of Mr. Khruschev himself in the liner *Baltika* from Russia to the U.S.A. developed the symbolism of an all-powerful force rolling towards a shocking climax of drama, and the Free World suspected the worst when it tried to probe mysteries of high policy which seemed to have run amuck.

Years must pass before the full story can be told because too many people are at present involved for more than an outline to be either possible or comprehensible. But even those facts which are known tax imagination to the limit and for some time official policy may deny their truth.

The fact remains that the special sessions of the United Nations during late 1960 ended with surprisingly little drama in spite of tub-thumping Communist histrionics during the early stages. Blood-curdling threats of world-shaking events which were hinted at by Moscow radio for Tuesday, 27 September were not fulfilled and the world's leaders returned to their palaces with surprisingly little to say for themselves.

That sort of thing cannot happen without powerful reasons and this book is the first to attempt an explanation. I do not claim that

1

it is accurate in detail, as the technicalities of new weapons are beyond my own understanding except in very general terms. A certain amount of deduction has also sometimes been necessary, but if this book is matched against news reports of the period it may explain just what did happen to make Khruschev panic and why he was so enraged. It will also explain why he once told the Americans that 'he would bury them' and it will clear up the mystery of those secret weapons to which he referred a short time later. This report also casts light upon certain momentous events in the Congo, Turkey and the Far East, and finally it explains why Francis Powers of ill-fated U.2 fame was the Last Spy before the brink of World War III.

The part played by myself has been trivial, and yet, in some respects, significant. After all, if I had not overheard the word 'anti-matter' in Moscow it might have been longer before more important people got to know about it. As for my own grilling and brain-washing experiences, the less I think of them the better, but I shall always be grateful to the late Professor Alexander Kennedy of Edinburgh for knowledge of how to survive the ordeal, and for information which also enabled me to discover a little of high drama.

I must further explain that the desire for anonymity by certain people has sometimes forced the use of fictitious names, but wherever that has been done the fact is noted by means of an asterisk and a footnote.

The explosion on Ritter Island has been described as a volcano. I have not been in that part of the world for several years and have had to rely upon the descriptions of others. If volcano is the wrong word then I apologize.

The Turkish Government is not likely to associate itself with any actions described in this book and the parts which may have been played by certain Turkish politicians were not used against them in their trials, the one who really mattered having committed suicide.

Probably Mr. Macmillan and the American President know more about events than any other Western statesmen. They will no doubt release what they consider to be wise in their own good time. Meanwhile, and until fully authentic data has been made avail-

2

able, this preliminary report may be of value in helping to condition the world towards later acceptance and disposal of those truly dreadful weapons with which it is now faced.

*　　*　　*

It may be helpful for readers to know that most of the dialogue in this report was written down as soon as possible after it took place. In certain places, naturally, the author has had to draw upon memory. On balance, however, the dialogue is accurate.

1

The first whisper

Moscow 1958 was crammed with visitors. Stalin had been disowned and Mr. Khruschev was wearing his New Look. Official spokesmen sang sweet songs of peace and tourists were being encouraged to go where they pleased. The Secret Police had become so secret that they had apparently ceased to exist and exclusive politicians were mixing freely with visitors at every Embassy party. According to *Pravda*, Moscow had become the Land of Smiles: but I was not inclined to believe one single word of it.

Not even when Shvernik himself, one of the old Bolsheviks and member of the Politburo, explained that the Soviet Union now wished only to live in peace with all her neighbours.

We were gossiping almost beneath the giant chandelier at Spaso House where the American Embassy was celebrating Independence Day. Many of New York's 400 were toasting everything and everybody in Caucasian champagne: beautiful women were using their wiles to shake the self-possession of lantern-jawed Comrades, whilst film stars, journalists and international opportunists were also there by the score, all rushing to exploit the new friendship which had so unexpectedly become possible.

Several, like myself, were collecting material for a book* and there was strong competition to meet celebrities, but my wife and I were being well looked after by a young English secretary who was quick off the mark. A small, plump man arrived with Gromyko the Foreign Minister. 'Serov himself,' the secretary whispered, 'Chief of the Security Police, once called O.G.P.U.'

* *Destination Moscow* (Herbert Jenkins 1960).

He was demoted a few months later, but at that time Serov was one of the top men in the country and skilfully holding down his job as Beria's successor. To look at him it was hard to believe that he had deported whole races, organized genocide and ordered the execution of thousands.

A Balkan military attaché then attracted Shvernik's attention and unconsciously gave me my chance with Gromyko. It is not rated bad manners to speak to the mighty without introduction at these diplomatic parties and in any case Gromyko seemed more approachable than usual. Of course, he is a disciplined individual at best and trained to keep a poker face in any company, but on that evening he was more relaxed and I decided that a blunt opening might pay dividends.

'Excuse me, sir,' I said. 'But has your Government really deviated from Marxist teaching and stopped trying to dominate the world either through war or revolution? Is this New Look business sincere?'

Perhaps my question took him by surprise. Perhaps he enjoyed springing a minor bomb, or perhaps he just felt like speaking the truth for once, but he heard me out and then stared hard for a full thirty seconds. His English is good when he cares to use it and his reply was slow but precise. 'You will know the answer quite soon. Watch the Middle East.'

A crowd was milling around us and a visitor had produced a flash camera. I would have expected Gromyko to be accustomed to photographers but he became irritable and a squabble developed as he tried to order the man away: which was hardly tactful since the American, strictly speaking, was in his own country.

In the midst of the argument I noticed Serov chatting with two other Americans. Their faces were smiling but Serov's eyes were hard as granite and the Americans seemed restless. I have always had a knack of being able to listen to two conversations at once . . . at least when I set my mind to it and get properly 'tuned in' . . . and fragments began to penetrate the buzz of argument. They were using an interpreter whose voice was pitched rather high, and at first nothing interesting came across, but then I heard one word which made me think.

'Anti-matter!'

6

The name was new to me but I did not care for its implications. It didn't look so good either when one studied eyes instead of faces, and I remembered Bernard Newman's advice: 'If you want to exchange confidences do so in a busy public place, where no one can overhear.'

'Who are these men?' I asked our secretary friend.

'As if you didn't know,' he said. 'Two of Uncle Sam's security boys. They are probably trying to pump the policeman. But excuse me a minute,' he added, 'there goes H.E. and I've got to pay my respects.' Sir Patrick Reilly, the British Ambassador, had arrived and our friend had to do the right thing by his sandy-haired chief.

Gromyko was still arguing with the photographer when Trudie, my wife, returned laden with sandwiches but still chatting to Shvernik. They were getting on well together and she was pressing our case for an appointment with Mr. Khruschev himself. In those days Mr. K. was not so free with his interviews and we had hoped to scoop his answers to a number of questions for our book, but Shvernik was not optimistic. 'Nikita is a busy man,' he explained, 'and your questions are difficult. But perhaps if you press him hard enough he'll see you. Anyhow it can do no harm to try.'

The old gentleman then shook hands and promised that he would do his best for us but he knew as well as we did that Nikita was unpredictable. Indeed he had been invited as guest of honour to the party that evening and had not turned up because he was annoyed with recent American policy. I had an idea that he would not receive anyone who was known to hob-nob with Americans and that our questions would remain unanswered. (As they did.)

But my attention was still riveted upon the Americans and upon General Ivan Alexandrovich Serov. In spite of their smiles the atmosphere seemed to be fairly crackling with tension and I decided to introduce myself. After all, I thought, if a cat can look at a king surely the K.V.B.* can hardly object if I try to chat with the boss-man.

The word 'anti-matter' had 'come through' a second time and it bothered me. It bothered me a lot, especially when I remembered

* Latest Soviet modification of the old O.G.P.U. or Secret Police.

7

that Serov was sixth in a dynasty of men who have wielded shocking power. The first was chief of Lenin's Cheka and 'died natural' in 1926. Menzhinsky was number two and he also died in bed after bringing the Cheka up to scratch as an organization for exterminating all opposition.

Yagoda, the third, was worst of all and ended by being executed himself after laying down a new pattern for torture and death without trial which had made every Russian tremble at the sound of his name.

Yagoda was evil, but the fourth was both mad and evil, Yezhov being Stalin's hatchet man who superintended the great purges and blazed a trail of tragedy unequalled by anyone since Genghis Khan.

Lavrenti Beria was number five and the only one to make a bid for total power. His end remains a mystery, because no one knows exactly when he died, but it is even rumoured that he was never tried at all and that Khruschev himself pulled the trigger on the night he was arrested.

Be that as it may, General Ivan Serov was a willing successor and I had to admit that the job did not seem to bother him. From a distance he seemed a complete extrovert and again I tried shock tactics.

'Pardon me, sir, but how about showing me round Lubianka Prison some time? It would be a newsy chapter for my Russian book.'

The interpreter laughed as he translated, and even Serov grinned. 'That is a capitalist rumour,' he said. 'Lubianka was Stalin's toy but now it is only a government office.'

(Which, incidentally, is completely untrue.)

The younger of the two Americans was holding a glass of champagne. Drinking toasts is an old Russian custom which the new U.S.S.R. still keeps up, and orgy by toast has become a favourite party game. It has also broken several junior diplomats and shaken the dignity of more than one ambassador who had not been taught how to play. Toasts are drunk straight with bottoms up every time and there are few recipes for survival except a steady head or inside knowledge of secrets. One easy way out is to bribe a waiter always to serve one with water rather than vodka. Another trick is to settle for white wine, which is less dangerous. But the rules allow your opponent to offer you a glass of his own choice and the only safe protection comes from a special pill. Activated charcoal taken an hour beforehand reduces the effect of alcohol and before long I was glad that both Trudie and I had each taken a couple, plus half a loaf of dry bread, well in advance.

A shot of vodka was thrust into my hand and the younger American raised his glass. 'To General Serov.'

Vodka is a coarse drink at best and I loathe it, but before I could reach for champagne the General had given me another.

'To our Allies,' he beamed. He had a trick of dropping his drink down his throat without swallowing and seemed to have a head like an ox.

The second American was quick off his mark, seized some hock and shouted, 'To Freedom.'

That one sounded near the bone until I remembered that in the complicated language of Communism 'freedom' means only the privilege of living under Marxian law and Kremlin discipline.

I got in first for the next round, lifted some glasses from a passing tray and hoped that my charcoal pills would work. 'To our great peoples,' I cried, knowing that no one can ever refuse to drink to our great peoples and that it meant less than nothing.

I had begun to realize that I was being made the target for an all-out attack but still had confidence in my pills and accepted two more toasts in the next ten minutes.

Then came 'To our glorious future' from Serov.

It had been bottoms up every time but now the strain was beginning to tell. One American was becoming slightly glazed. His fingers were trembling and his speech was thick. The other was bright-eyed and smiling fixedly. Serov himself was flushing red but with twinkling laughter lines which invited me to do my worst.

It was my honour again, and as I handed over three more glasses of vodka it was good to see that my hands were steady, co-ordination under control and voice normal.

Impulse is rarely a wise counsellor but not for worlds would I have missed the chance which was offering. 'To anti-matter,' I said and raised my own glass of pink champagne.

It was a bull's-eye. Three glasses paused in mid-air and the General spoke rapidly to his interpreter. 'His Excellency did not understand your toast. Explain, please, and at once.'

I have a memory of pasty faces and sweating brows in the background, of soft music coming from a portable radio and of a girl's voice giggling in the distance. But otherwise there seemed to be complete silence. Serov's eyes were boring into my very consciousness and the Americans were looking at me with something near hate.

Oddly enough none of the three glasses moved and it was as though they had been fixed for ever in cataleptic immobility. But more frightening was Serov's tightly drawn face, a set to his jaw and those impersonal eyes which simply . . . looked. And looked. And looked until I felt like screaming.

I dare say it was all over in a few seconds, because in spite of surprise my wits were working overtime and somehow produced an excuse. Retrospectively it may have been a fatuous excuse but it had the merit of being true in essentials. Forcing a smile I looked away from the General and turned to the interpreter, who was standing with one fist clenched and as though ready to strike me.

'My mother has six sisters and one brother. The eighth child on her side of the family was called Gretta and I once promised her that no matter where I might be the eighth toast of any evening would be drunk to her honour. This is now my custom and I am sorry if it seems eccentric. But I also ask you to join in drinking to . . . my Auntie Gretta.'

The interpreter swiftly translated and the three men looked at me suspiciously. 'You are a bloody liar,' said one of the Americans.

His friend leaned forward. His speech was slurred and his eyes bloodshot. 'Do better than that next time, Limey. What do you know?'

Soviet interpreters are efficient and so well do they work that at times one is hardly aware they exist. 'Gentlemen,' said Serov, 'that is all. Let us drink to the Scottish lady . . . Auntie Gretta.'

The most improbable things in this world are often true. Who would have believed that Mr. Khruschev in 1960 would receive an apple pie loaded with a copy of the Ten Commandments, or that American police would remove it in a bomb-proof van and that it would make world television headlines!

The same sense of the ridiculous almost made me choke on my wine when I realized that the Chief of Russia's Secret Police . . . or its modern equivalent . . . was drinking to my conventional aunt in distant Scotland.

The Americans were slow at first to move, and then one of them lifted his arm. 'What the hell anyhow. Here's to Gretta, and if it wasn't to Gretta it would be to some other dame.'

The General prepared to go but first he had a word for the Americans. 'You are almost drunk. Do something about it.'

They faced him like sulky children. His eyes were now curiously dead-pan. 'I suggest that you go to bed.'

They slouched off with a curt nod and Trudie joined me when she saw that I was being left alone with the General. Nothing much ever misses her and she had sensed trouble. Serov is said to have an attraction for women. He is also interested in them and the temperature rose slightly when I introduced her.

'My husband is trying to arrange an interview with Mr. Khruschev,' said Trudie. 'Could you put in a word for him?'

Tension relaxed. 'You may be certain, ma'am, that I shall tell Mr. Khruschev all about your husband.'

When he shook hands his fingers felt flabby and his palms were wet with sweat. 'Perhaps we might show you Lubianka after all,' he smiled. And then Trudie and I were alone.

'I don't like that man,' she said. 'He smells of death.'

I was not sure how much she had overheard or guessed and I did not want to spoil things. It was easier to say nothing and to pass the rest of the evening with other less dangerous people.

But I was uneasy for the rest of our stay in Moscow and expected trouble. Everything went smoothly, however, until the second last day when we visited the Industrial Exhibition, which is a Moscow 'must' and surely the finest permanent exhibition in the world.

We were studying one of the early Sputniks in the Pavilion of Science when I met one of the American security men. Someone had said that their names were Martin and Mitchell but I never knew the one from the other and we were never introduced.

I would make a bad diplomat. The blunt approach is my forte and nothing could have stopped me trying it again. 'What do you know about anti-matter?' I said.

He was as surprised to see me as I had been to meet him and a pulse had mounted in his neck. 'Suppose you tell me.'

'Right. You were speaking about it with Serov. You mentioned it twice. You jumped as though you had been shot when I used it as a toast. Serov hinted that drunks talk too much and ordered you to bed. Would you by any chance be doing a Fuchs and selling the U.S.A. up the creek?'

But he had collected his wits and become rock steady . . . except for the pulse in his neck which was running at a steady hundred plus. 'Serov was only trying to pump us about Ike's security arrangements for a visit that's in the offing.'

'What visit?'

'Mr. Big is thinking about crossing the Pond.'

'So you never used the word anti-matter?'

''sright.'

'Well, now you are the liar because I heard you say it twice.'

For a moment he blustered. How the hell could a guy remember what he said at a party where everybody was half drunk? And what was I playing up about anyhow? So far as he was concerned I could take a censored powder and scram.

He then stubbed his cigarette and paused for a long minute during which his manner became completely different. 'O.K. There is stuff called anti-matter. But how come *you* know about it? You're a bloody Limey and your government hasn't one single solitary dime's worth of dope about it. Maybe you heard a rumour or maybe you're just playing the hand close to your chest. But take a tip and watch your step. Anti-matter isn't stuff for amateurs.'

That evening I hinted to one of our own Secretaries that two American security men seemed bad risks and sounded him about anti-matter. He had never heard of it and suggested that I had been reading too much space fiction. Martin and Mitchell . . . if these were the names . . . were O.K.

Next morning two things happened.

Radio news headlined the revolution in Iraq. The King had been murdered and his family butchered. Gromyko's words had acquired meaning. 'You will know the answer quite soon. Keep your eyes on the Middle East.'

No answer could have been clearer. Russia had not given up her programme of world domination through war or revolution. This time it was revolution. Perhaps the next shot would be war!

The New Look was phoney.

And on the same morning coincidence played a part when a Zim car stopped beside us at traffic lights near Zubosvkaya Square. There were four men in the back, Serov's interpreter, the same two Americans and Bruno Pontecorvo, the scientist who went 'red' and who was then directing Soviet research into nuclear weapons. Pontecorvo was unmistakable and holding an old leather brief-case under the arm of a Western-style suit. All were looking finely drawn and serious.

I hoped only that they had failed to recognize us or spot our car, which was a conspicuous Volkswagen, and probably the only one in Moscow.

'What's the matter?' asked Trudie.

Again it seemed easier not to bother her. We had two long motoring days ahead before the frontier and Serov could pick us off anywhere he wished between Moscow and East Berlin.

The frontier, however, was easy. Formalities in fact were practically non-existent and I didn't like that either, especially when I remembered the old Russian saying: 'Never do murder in your own garden.' But Poland might be dangerous and our next stop was Warsaw.

Iron Curtain visas are almost fool-proof and we were scheduled to cross certain frontiers at specified places, but I guessed it was safer to take a chance on that so we cut south to Cracow, stayed for one night and then entered Czechoslovakia on the main route to Brno. We then lost ourselves in Prague before pointing west for Trasenau (Drazenov) and on to the easiest crossing on record into West Germany. The chance had come off and frontier officials accepted our reasons for altering our route.

Every traveller familiar with the Communist Satellites knows the sense of relief which arrives after crossing a frontier with the West. It is as though a great burden of oppression had been removed from one's deepest soul. And for a while one really does understand the meaning of the word freedom. West Germany felt like Paradise. But only for a couple of days and until we started once more to prove a point.

2

The girl in velvet jeans

DONAUWÖRTH is a happy small town on the Danube. But like many other German towns it has plenty of secrets. Our friends there had suffered under Hitler. One had been a prisoner of war in Canada, the second had endured two years in Dachau and Hanna, his wife, had been saved only at the last minute from Ravensbrück's gas chambers. People like that know the ropes. Each in his own way had forged friendships with strange people and all were bound by that loyalty which comes only from dangers shared.

Hans Richter* is a quiet, tubby little man with close-cropped hair who likes his beer and salami. He could never be mistaken for anything other than a German but his bovine manner conceals a razor-sharp brain and an enviable capacity for survival. Indeed he survived Dachau only because he made himself useful in winkling out gold from the teeth of the dead, melting it down and moulding tiny swastikas. His macabre hobby appealed to the guards and the gold swastikas fetched high prices in Berlin's night-clubs. Later he turned his hand to medicine and became an orderly in the camp hospital. He even helped the doctors in their euthanasia experiments and what he did not learn about human nature isn't worth knowing.

But throughout it all he continued to work for the German Underground, acted as undercover man in the exchange of Jewish prisoners and personally removed a few stool-pigeons introduced into the camps by Himmler.

* An unavoidable pseudonym since he is still engaged in counter-espionage.

In the end he came out knowing everybody, feared by a few, respected by a select group of agents and despised by all the rest. He then drifted back into apparent obscurity in his own home town where he wriggled up to the neck in deeper intrigue than ever.

Today he is an authority on East Berlin and is wanted more than almost any other man by Walter Ulbricht, the President of the Democratic Republic. He is also called in from time to time to do one of the most distasteful jobs open to any German.

Camp Valka, on the outskirts of Nuremberg, is still West Germany's chief receiving centre for refugees. It is a miserable place, draughty and rotten with both age and memory. In fact Bonn should be ashamed of it. The people who arrive there have risked life itself to escape from the Communists and yet their first taste of a Free World is Valka, where close upon nine months is needed, upon average, to screen them. Hans screens certain suspects.

'Yes,' he said sadly. 'Valka is bad. But we cannot let up on screening. The East keeps sending traitors to act as another Fifth Column and that is where I can be useful. Dachau taught me to smell these people a mile away so when there is doubt they ask me up.'

'That means you are still in touch with everything which is going on behind the scenes in East Germany?'

'Sure. But Valka also has people from all over Eastern Europe.'

'Has anyone ever hinted at new weapons?'

'They are always mentioning new weapons. Nerve gases: bacterial bombs: anything which they hope will help us to accept them quickly.'

'You seem sceptical.'

'Naturally. If Russia or Ulbricht wanted to plant a spy the last thing he would wish to do would be to attract attention. The others are small fry, and any real big man will be known to our people. His name will *mean* something.'

'But don't you pay attention to rumour?'

'I live by rumour. And I try to keep Germany safe by being guided by rumour. But I don't listen to rumours about secret weapons.'

'Why not?'

'Because the people with whom I deal could not possibly know

16

anything about secret blue-prints. And once a new weapon leaves the blue-print stage so many people get to know about it that it is no longer secret.'

'Does the word anti-matter mean anything?'

He puffed quietly at his bubbling clay pipe, and then: 'Tell me more.'

'It might be the name of some new Bolshie horror.'

Hans has a pleasant reassuring manner. 'In fact,' said Trudie on one occasion, 'he is a sort of mental poultice to reduce tension.'

But when his voice becomes particularly gentle it always means that he is interested. 'Memory is a funny thing,' he said, 'and psychiatrists talk about word association. Your word anti-matter reminds me of a young man called Helmut Gröttrup who worked in Peenemünde and helped to develop our first V.2. He always thought of it as a step towards space flight and had advanced ideas about the possibilities of atomic fission. In those days we spoke about chain reactions and expected the whole world to blow up but Helmut laughed at pessimists and said that if you could use atomic power properly there was no end to its potentialities. He believed that it might even destroy matter itself or change it into energy. Vaguely I remember that he explained how a by-product might one day be found which could be called anti-matter.'

'Where is Gröttrup now?'

Hans slowly rubbed his row of chins and his voice became more gentle than ever. 'The Russians took him over in 1945. The Americans had offered him a contract but refused permission for his wife and family to accompany him to the States. The Russians were more generous and gave him a huge salary. He worked on liquid fuels and after a while was removed to Russia. He returned to Germany in 1953 when he was no further use to them and my last news said that he was looking for work in Munich.'

'But he used the word anti-matter towards the end of the war.'

'Not towards the end. Just before I went to Dachau. Say the middle of the war.'

'And he may have spoken about it to the Russians?'

'Very well,' said Hans. 'Hanna, Josef and myself will do what we can. We shall keep our ears open.'

'And changing the subject,' I said, 'what about your friend Ulbricht? Would the East German Government know anything about new Soviet discoveries?'

'No. Ulbricht's record of treachery is too much for even Khruschev to stomach gladly. Think of it. He betrayed scores of old comrades starting with Ernst Thälmann whom he sold to Hitler as far back as 1933: later he sold them to Nazis and Communists alike . . . and even to the Allies during the war. He is the greatest living Judas, and I never forget that when speaking of Beria, Khruschev on one occasion also said of Ulbricht: "His time will come."'

'So any new devices are more likely to be developed in Russia.'

'Or possibly in the Balkans.'

'For example?'

'I am told that things are happening along the Russian coast south of Constanța and Albania, of course, is completely sealed. There are rumours of activity in Bulgaria and I would take a bet that top-level planning continues in Prague. It is the clearing-house between West and East, and if you want advance news of Soviet intrigue it is always wise to keep an eye on the Czech press.'

'But you have no other clues about anti-matter?'

'None.'

As he spoke his eyes were studying the lights on the other side of the river. 'It is a beautiful night,' he said. 'The Danube may not be blue but it is always lovely and a stroll before bed would be pleasant.'

The bill was settled and we returned from the terrace towards the cloak-room. A girl was reading *Paris Match* as we passed through the hall and for a moment our eyes met. Calculating, impersonal and hard they held me for a long second and then she returned to her book. Her legs were the most exquisite things in southern Germany and her figure left little to the imagination. A long pair of blue velvet jeans clung to her thighs like a glove and ended in a flow of deeply tanned skin which ran into golden flip-flops. A taut wine-coloured blouse proved high-set breasts thrusting forward below a golden chain and tiny crucifix. She wore no make-up and her fingernails were tinted to match her footwear.

Hans did not seem to notice her and in the moonlight beyond

took me gently by the arm. 'Let us look at the river. It encourages sleep.'

For a long time he said nothing. And then: 'Hanna and I have a simple arrangement. If she wishes to contact me without fuss she lights our attic window. Tonight it was alight for ten seconds before I suggested this little walk so there will be news when we return home. But first, we shall keep to our programme and look at the river.'

'Without talking,' I added.

'We shall not talk,' he agreed.

Half an hour later we arrived at his house. Hanna was preparing *Apfelstrudl* . . . one of our favourite dishes . . . and coffee was in the percolator. 'You are being watched by a girl,' she said.

'A beautiful girl?'

'A girl without a soul. Her eyes are dead. Her body is alive. She is too interested in you.'

'Did Trudie see her?' I asked.

'Trudie discovered her. She says that she saw her for the first time in Moscow when you visited the House of Tolstoi. She says that the girl was then walking with two men she had earlier noticed at the American Embassy party. We saw her watching you in the hotel and Trudie says it cannot be coincidence.'

My wife has a fine instinct which so far has never let me down.

'Moreover,' continued Trudie, 'I am sure that one of the men she was with in Moscow left Spaso House along with Serov. He was one of the background people whom nobody spoke to whilst the General was stealing the limelight.'

'And our Tolstoi visit was arranged through Intourist.'

'Yes. So they could easily have taken that girl along and pointed us out to her when we arrived.'

'The situation is unsatisfactory,' said Hanna, 'but I booked a room for you in the hotel starting as from tomorrow, so that will keep the girl happy for tonight at least. I have also packed your car. Tonight you will move on. Hans will tell me the story and by tomorrow you will be far away.'

A long night run had no attractions, but Hanna's judgment is shrewd. We pulled out the car at 2 a.m. and two days later were in Holland after an uneventful journey.

19

Shortly before Christmas an unsigned letter reached us from Germany.

It was crisp and to the point. 'I know nothing.' But a tiny piece had been torn from one corner and on the back there was a small irregular blot . . . signature of our friends.

Anti-matter remained a mystery, and the girl an even greater mystery which was not solved until the following summer when we arranged a Balkan trip to search for further pieces of the jig-saw puzzle.

I had, however, one clue. One or two of my physicist friends had made cautious reference to shattering developments which might lie around the corner in their own fields of nuclear fission.

The man who knew most was cagey, however, and all I could get out of him was a vague suggestion that it might be possible to detonate an atomic weapon without immediately releasing its explosive effects: that the detonated bomb might then be held in some sort of container which could have the effect of reinforcing its destructive power. His staff believed that the ultimate weapon might be an artificial satellite travelling in orbit at approximately earth's own speed but placed like a permanent artificial moon above the selected target. The ideal height above earth would be something less than 100 miles and its speed would, therefore, have to be a shade faster than the earth's rotation in order for it to remain in a fixed position relative to the target area. Very fine calculations would be needed to achieve this, but success was possible, and if such an artificial satellite, sputnik, or call it what one wished, were to be loaded with an appropriately destructive weapon any nation might be obliged, literally, to live under the shadow of sudden death.

I had also learned more of the missile bases then being constructed along part of the Roumanian sea-board and hoped that the Balkan tour would enable us to get a whiff of whatever might be brewing.

Unfortunately I played my cards badly. It is usually better to visit a trouble spot with official backing and I made an approach to the Roumanian Government for permission to photograph the former Royal Palaces, the Presidential Palace in Bucharest and various other Ruritanian hangovers from the past.

At first things moved smoothly. Ion Dumitru, Secretary to the London Legation, was affable. He even apologized for the rule which obliged visitors to carry with them an official guide-interpreter. We drank good coffee at No. 4, Palace Green and I listened to him lecture on the difficulties of his posting. Although only Secretary he was actually in charge and he was homesick. Roumanians were not popular in London and the job was difficult.

Our tour was then arranged in detail and I left assured of Government backing. Visas would be automatic.

Two months later a curt letter advised me that 'The Roumanian Government cannot assure services'. A reply which meant, in effect, nothing doing.

The deal was off, but since I was due to free-lance for the *Glasgow Evening Citizen*, Norris Smythe, the Features Editor, contacted the United Press, which turned on a certain amount of heat. But the deal was still off and they learned only that I had probably erred in making an official approach, that I might have fared better by trying to go as a straightforward tourist booking through 'Progressive Tours, London'.

Progressive Tours are specialists in handling Eastern European visas and were, in fact, handling our affairs, but the combined efforts of Mrs. A. L. Lowe, the secretary, and Director Sofka Skipwith failed in our case to produce anything for Roumania.

As a consolation prize we opted instead for Bulgaria and decided to press on to Turkey from where we could explore much of the Black Sea coast at leisure.

Roads from Rotterdam east are good and we paused only in Vienna and Budapest. The mountain crossing from Nis to Dimitrovgrad was made through the long twilight of a lovely evening and we arrived at Sofia in time for late dinner in the Balkan Hotel.

Sofia is a magnificent city. Its post-war buildings are the most exciting in Eastern Europe, and a cunning blend of modern architectural idioms with mosques and minarets has made something really worthwhile. It is probably the most attractive capital city east of Vienna . . . always excepting Moscow, of course, which still stands alone.

We were keen to attend the Opera House but tickets were sold out and a concert of national folk music on the following evening was open only through invitation. There was nothing interesting at any of the other theatres. Sofia looked like being a cultural vacuum for the Mairs when one of the hotel staff suddenly produced seats for the concert.

On the following morning my wife opted to look up an old contact who was passing through to Athens by car and to explore the shops with her, meeting me only in time for dinner.

Less than five minutes after she left the hotel a young man introduced himself. His English was good and he had been sent, he explained, by the opera management to ask if we would be its guests for the day. It was known that we were attending in the evening and the manager wished to show us the sights. A car was at my disposal and the young man, Hristo by name, would be proud to accompany me.

A trip to Boyana Church and Mount Vitosha was suggested. Boyana has some fine tenth-century paintings, and I had not made the circuit of Vitosha by Stoudena Dam to Samokov. I liked the idea. Hristo was a jovial character and there was ample time to return for dinner with Trudie.

Vitosha Mountain is attractive country and as we swept along the Boulevard Tolboukhin it loomed ahead like some of our Perthshire hills. But many parts of Bulgaria resemble Scotland and I was brooding about the similarity even amongst some of the people when the car stopped in a side street by a block of new flats.

'My home,' explained Hristo apologetically. 'I must tell my wife that I do not come back for lunch.'

A moment later he returned smiling apologetically. 'I am sorry and my wife says that I have no manners. Perhaps you have not been inside a Bulgarian house. Would you care to join us for coffee? We have a new baby and my wife wants everyone to look at it. She is very excited about the new baby. It weighed almost five kilos at birth, very, very big. And strong. So strong you would not believe it.'

Of course I went with him. Wouldn't you?

And as we entered his house the first person I saw was the girl with the blue velvet jeans.

'Come right in,' she said. 'I have been waiting to meet you for a long time.'

22

3

Paula Stoicheva

THE room was quite small, not more than twelve feet square. The walls were papered with a pinkish floral design and the floor laid with thick crimson carpets. The ceiling was terracotta and heavy brown curtains covered the windows. They were closed and two wall-lights gave a comfortable sense of intimacy.

Furnishings were sparse; one large divan, two lug chairs and an oak refectory-type table with massive top and heavy broad legs. There were no ornaments other than a hanging clock which ticked heavily, and it was exactly ten-seventeen.

A door flush with one wall was paper-covered like the rest of the room, and concealed lighting had been laid on right round above the picture rail. Only one picture was hanging, a smallish oil of a young man struggling to cross a barbed-wire fence. The background was dark but in one corner a searchlight played upon the scene and a running soldier was firing from the hip.

Naturally I did not see all this at once. But I was to become familiar with the place in all its changing moods.

The girl was looking at me dispassionately. She wore a thin cotton dress and might have been a teenager off for a walk in the park. Her legs were still tanned and a tightly drawn leather belt showed that she was still proud of her figure.

'Suppose you sit down,' she smiled.

'Suppose you explain,' I suggested, looking at Hristo. For the first time in my life I knew the meaning of fear. Real fear. The kind of fear which chills the bowels and sends tingling shivers up one's spine to every single hair follicle on the scalp. That fear which makes one sick inside and think of a winter's day at home, of the fireside and morning paper, of children squabbling and the noise of housework in the next room, all those cosy simple things which are suddenly precious . . . when about to be lost.

'I brought you here to have a talk.'

'And is this lady your wife?'

'No, but we shall have coffee just the same.'

'Will you not introduce me?'

He smiled a little but refused. 'She will introduce herself when she wishes. Meanwhile you must understand that you are in an awkward position. You have been brought here for a reason and when or how you leave will depend upon yourself. My people are generous to everyone who assists them, but they treat enemies harshly.'

'What makes you think that I could assist you in any way?'

'Since leaving Russia you have given many popular lectures on Moscow. On the whole you have been fair. You have told people of many "good things" which appealed to you. Other criticism has been objective and this is so unusual that we feel you might be educated into appreciating even those things you have criticized.'

'How?'

'By learning the reasons for them. By understanding more about the problems which face our people.'

'And if I learn more about these problems?'

'You are a professional man with some status and authority. Your word counts with quite large numbers of your countrymen. They would believe whatever you might say next winter, or the next again, in your lecture programmes.'

'So I could have a propaganda value.'

'That is so.'

'My lectures earn fees without any special political slant. What would a good stiff dose of pro-Communist propaganda be worth?'

Hristo studied me thoughtfully. 'You have no obvious weak spots. But every man has a weak spot somewhere. Usually it is power, money or women. What would be your fee?'

'If I were convinced that your people had the correct answer to

24

living, that they could resolve international tension overnight, I would work for nothing.'

'But you don't believe that?'

'No. I believe instead that every single international problem is due to Soviet trouble-makers and Marxian bull combined. If you wanted to relieve international tension Khruschev and the Russian leaders could do it overnight. But you don't. You want instead to foment trouble in every weak spot, to prove the Western defences until you find the crack which may break. And you want to rule the world from Moscow. Your only real fear is that the world may be ruled instead from Peking.'

Hristo's voice became spiteful. 'Right. Well, suppose we talk not about propaganda but about anti-matter?'

Almost it felt good to know the worst at last. There was even satisfaction in having proof that the stuff was important.

'What makes you think that I know anything about it?'

He raised his hands in an expressive gesture of distaste. 'Don't waste time. A man doesn't behave as you have done, being heavy-handed and tactless, unless he is either a fool or else is so clever that he wishes to be taken for a fool.'

'What has that got to do with it?'

'To use a British proverb. You have barged in where angels fear to tread. You pretend to be a tactless oaf. But you are not. You are a clever man and clever men don't waste their time.'

'And are you clever?'

'I am extremely clever. And I have been given the job of finding out what you know about anti-matter.'

'Your English is very good. Where did you learn it?'

'I was an interpreter for Americans after the war. I have also worked in our London Embassy.'

'"Our"?'

'My country is not your affair.'

'What is my affair?'

'Your life. And perhaps the life of your wife.'

'And if I tell you that anti-matter is only a name to me?'

'None of us will believe you.'

'How many are in the "us"?'

'Let me speak to him,' said the girl. Her voice was deeply pitched, almost husky, and as she approached she unexpectedly held out her hand. We were still standing and the clock said ten-eighteen. I suppose some things are done automatically but it was impossible not to be polite. As we shook hands I felt that her skin was cool and soft. Her eyes were faintly smiling. Almost she seemed friendly and in that cotton rig-out seemed no more dangerous than a schoolgirl catching butterflies.

'Last time you looked much more sophisticated,' I said.

'Last time you were very clever,' she corrected.

Hristo was watching us with a curiously cynical twist to his mouth. 'Do you wish me to go?'

The girl nodded. 'You might finish making our coffee.'

My hands were in my trouser pockets. A few coins jangled as I fidgeted with my fingers. And then they touched something. A small ovoid capsule. For many years I have occasionally used one and a half grains of seconal as a sleeping pill and had intended to take this one on the previous night if necessary. But after a good dinner and pleasant talk there had been no need. Now it was in my hand and if I could use it things would feel better. A lot better.

As she watched Hristo step through the wall door I slipped the capsule between the ball of my thumb and tip of my index finger.

'Do sit down,' she said and pointed to the divan.

I hitched up my trousers, and as she turned to adjust a cushion managed to slip the pill into my mouth.

For a while she simply sat and looked at me. And then she laughed. 'You have a face like thunder. Why don't you relax and make the best of things? I don't look so frightening, do I? And when you hear my story you will understand.'

And the clock said ten-twenty.

Time had never passed so slowly. Only three minutes since I had come into the room! I had begun to pull myself together although the seconal had not yet had time to work. But I still felt squeamish. Fear was still nagging my guts and my fingers were shaking when I lit a cigarette. But now I believed that I could control the fear. I knew also that I was up against the biggest thing in my life and that if I did not play my cards properly I might even die. I realized too that Trudie might die, that we might never see

26

our children again or gather flowers in Dunira, watch the autumn heather or pitch snowballs in February, that this might be the end. But I also knew that I had found strength to make it a good end if necessary and that I would give them a run for their money.

'Let me explain,' she said. 'And when Hristo brings coffee you can take your choice of cup. This is an armistice to be used for straightening things out.'

'I'm listening.'

'Somehow you have discovered about anti-matter, and when you were in Moscow you guessed that General Serov was also interested. You tried bluff, and it worked because the Americans were taken by surprise. But you were very smart and your explanation was just possible. In fact you wouldn't have left Russia at all if it had been a lie, but within three days we had checked your story and discovered your Auntie Gretta working in her Rutherglen garden along with her sisters Chrissie, Mina and Isa. We also proved that she had been the eighth child. The General then decided that because of all the noise going on at the party he really had mistaken your words. He was even big enough to leave it at that, so you didn't see Lubianka after all. If you hadn't spoken again to the American at the Exhibition things would have still been left alone. But that conversation showed that you were important. We then decided to pick you up somewhere in Poland, but once more you deceived us and disappeared through Prague into Germany. I can also tell you that the frontier security men concerned have been disciplined for allowing you out at a place different from the exit point stamped on your visa. Life is being made easy for tourists but not all that easy, and regulations must be enforced in spite of our "New Look".

'You were exactly thirty-five hours ahead of us all the way from Warsaw. But you were lucky and, to tell you the truth, I am superstitious. I like lucky people because often they bring me luck.'

'Will I bring you luck?'

She eased herself back on the divan. Her frock was crumpling around her thighs and her knees were drawn under her like a child. Her hair glinted warm in the cosy light and her pouting lips were an invitation. 'You might,' she said. 'I hope so.'

27

'How did you reach Donauwörth?'

'You left an easy trail. Coffee in Rötz, luncheon at the Grüner Kranz in Regensburg, gas and oil at Abbach and tea near Ingolstadt. Obviously you would stop at Donauwörth for dinner.'

'The hotel meeting was coincidence?'

'Sure. But we were both in Donauwörth so we were pretty certain to meet. It is not large.'

'But you fell for our bluff?'

'I was deceived. Yes.'

'And when did you prepare this welcome?'

'We decided to watch you during the winter. We know all about your lectures. You also spoke to two physicists, one radiologist, three engineers and various technicians who work with electronics. You tried to pump them all and got news of some sort from at least one.'

'How do you know all this?'

'Because, as you have hinted elsewhere, the world is filled with our agents. Each works under a supreme director. Ernst Wollweber, for example, has at least 9,000 official staff members and perhaps 50,000 undercover agents for his work in directing East German security. General Serov has supreme control over at least ten times that number. You forget that one of our basic principles is to profess "false creeds in order to win positions of importance or influence". Anacharsis Cloots wrote that years ago but it is still true. In fact it applies more today than ever before.'

'And one of these busy people was detailed to keep an eye on me?'

'No. One of them knows you quite well. He is not an intimate friend but you meet from time to time and since you talk too much he is well informed.'

'Tell me more about your agents?'

'We have a few in the Tory Party and more than thirty in your Parliamentary Labour Party. We control at least three major British trade unions and our cousins in Britain are worth their weight in gold.'

'Brothers or comrades surely?' I said, trying hard to joke but feeling sick as Hell.

'The name is not important. The really important fact is that nothing can happen anywhere without us knowing.'

I could guess the rest. The Roumanians, Bulgars, everyone, knew that we were off to the Balkans. Our trouble with the Roumanians had even been written up in the newspapers and we had been sitting ducks from the instant we had crossed the Hungarian frontier at Hegyeshalom. But why wait until Sofia before pulling me in? And where was my wife?

'Sofia suited me.'

'Why?'

'My name is Paula Stoicheva,' she said. 'I lived here with my brother Petko before the war. Petko was killed by the British when attempting to escape from a prisoner-of-war camp in Italy and I like to think that his soul came back to the place where we had known such good times.'

'And?' She was watching me like a cat.

'When I want to kill a British person I like to do it in Sofia. Also our people have created facilities for privacy here. This is a receiving centre for suspects.'

Abruptly she left the room. I was alone. The clock was still ticking and it said ten-twenty-eight.

It is easy for some critics to tell me what I should have done. Strong-arm fiction heroes would have broken out to safety with a few swift uppercuts and one deft throw of the small knife kept up one sleeve for that very purpose. In real life things work out differently. I was forty-five and liked to think that I was as fit as most men of thirty. But I do not fight wild cats. And I do not fight men half my age who look as though they could take care of themselves.

My only chance of coming out alive seemed to lie in a battle of wits. And I had at least one asset. The seconal capsule was beginning to work and might keep me fairly calm. One and a half grains normally knocks me flat over to sleep when travelling on a train or in a storm at sea. I have used nothing else for twenty years, and although I might take only one or two per month some tolerance has developed and its sleeping effect would be offset by tension. I was still scared, but expected to be left cool enough to behave properly, and clear-headed enough to think properly.

29

I am also fortunate in thinking fast and reacting well to an emergency, and already a convincing story was beginning to germinate. Given another hour or two the egg would be laid.

Hour or two! The clock showed that I had been in the place for only half an hour, and this seemed impossible until I remembered Alex Kennedy of Edinburgh who had once mentioned a device for rattling people about to be questioned. Put them in a room with a clock and adjust the clock to go very slowly but yet with the pendulum swinging at normal speed.

My pulse was doing about ninety to the minute.

Eagerly I watched the minute hand.

The thing was haywire. Calculated against a pulse of even seventy-two it was still haywire.

In the end I decided that for every minute which it recorded two and a half to three had actually passed.

After that I felt better. Not much. But still better.

And then the lady returned with coffee. 'Forgive me,' she said. 'I was angry and it would not have been fair to take it out on you. Although I still hate Britain for killing my brother.'

Her eyes turned to the picture on the wall. 'He was twenty-four when he died.'

'Older than you.'

'Much. I was sixteen at the time.'

'So now you are in the early thirties?'

'Getting old,' she agreed.

Hristo had left us alone. I had caught a glimpse of him when the door opened. There were several people in the next room, two of them girls.

The coffee was good and the atmosphere of the room had somehow warmed, with walls, floors and ceiling just a shade richer under sensuous lighting.

And then I saw that the concealed strip lights had started to glow, that their effect was to make the whole room palely crimson and that even the girl's clothes were reflecting its richness. The temperature had also begun to rise and a bead of sweat gathered on my palm. It was almost enjoyable to sit in such a place. The girl was once more charming. The cushion was comfortable. Fear had slipped away and I was almost relaxed.

'This is a pleasant armistice,' I said.

'It will be as pleasant as you care to make it.'

There was another long silence broken only by the monotonous click-clack of that wall clock. The steady noise was getting on my nerves. Even the pendulum was annoying, a golden blob moving to and fro on the pink wall just in front of me. To the right there was nothing but the oil-painting. And it was better not to look too much to the left towards a woman who was beginning to put off her mask.

Her lovely tan swept down from her oval face into a long slim neck and lost itself, lightening in the creamy skin above her breasts. She had changed her frock and now wore a loose housecoat affair which sagged every time she leaned forward to drop ash or lift a cup. Her long thighs were glinting provocatively below a slackly bound waistbelt, and frills of fluffy lace curled above the elbow round each short sleeve.

It took no great brain to see that a seduction routine lay just ahead. But only a demented imagination could have visualized how she would play it.

'I think I will put my cards on the table,' said Paula. 'The armistice is over.'

4

The men who were tortured

'Hristo said that you were clever and I agree with him. So we have given you long enough to judge the position. Either you talk or suffer.'

'And if I do talk?'

'You live. You might even do well out of it.'

'How well?'

She smiled. 'I am an experienced woman. Frankly you appeal to me, and many men would think that a night with myself was enough.'

'One night?'

'Perhaps more. It depends on how much you please me. Upon your technique.'

'Technique?'

'Are you a conventional lover?' She was watching me with a weird concentration which was frightening. Her eyes were again cool, almost impartial and yet somehow calculating. She was breathing more heavily and as she leaned forward her house-coat again flopped open to reveal those thrusting breasts whose milky skin contrasted with the walnut tan of chest and limbs.

She sat, motionless for perhaps a minute, studying me as a dealer might consider some doubtful item at a sale. 'I don't want you to make any mistake. Tell us everything you know about anti-matter and then you can come to me. I can be a mistress you would never forget.'

'I don't want girls. I am happily married.'

She was quick to flush. Indeed this was her only give-away signal. And as she flushed her right hand crashed across my mouth. Her ring drew blood at the edge of my lower lip and the scar still disfigures it.

'Madame!'

Hristo's voice was urgent. I had not heard him arrive but now he was in the room and he spoke with authority. 'Patience. First we talk. Please control yourself.'

The girl paused, fumbled for a cigarette and then clicked a lighter. I was taken off guard. Before she closed it the tiny flame had crossed my fingers and left a thin line of charred fair hair above a first-degree burn.

'Very well,' she said. 'Ask him or tell him whatever you like, Hristo, but then give him to me.'

The man sat down on a chair by my side. The room was now cold and I am sure that there was a device for controlling temperature. 'Try and be sensible,' he said. 'You can tell us something. We have proved that we know quite a lot about your activities. It will pay you to be frank.'

'Because if I don't the lady will beat me up?'

'Paula is an unusual girl,' said Hristo. 'After the war she worked in some of our camps and was trained by the famous commandant Piroshka at Recsk. Piroshka was ingenious and liked to do unusual things to men. Paula was her best pupil.'

'But if I say what you wish?' My voice was quivering and I was scared again. Not by Hristo but by the sight of the girl. She had slipped off her house-coat. Her figure was superb but she watched me as a snake watches a bird and the hint of sexual violence which surrounded her was terrifying.

Hristo did not even look at her. 'She would be a mistress you could never forget. We would even pay you well in money. You could move freely through all of the Communist Empire and be treated as an honoured friend.' He paused for a second and then pointed towards Paula. 'She has wanted you ever since she saw you at Donauwörth. What man could refuse such a gift? Tell us what you know and I will leave you together.'

This was the pay-off. It might decide life or death. But a streak of obstinacy in me still refused even a lie. 'I know nothing.'

The girl leapt across the room and opened the wall door. 'Bring him in,' she cried.

33

Hristo had walked backwards towards the curtain and seemed pale even in the crimson light of the place.

A hospital-type trolley was wheeled in by two girls. A man was clamped to it by leather straps. He was wholly naked and his powerful body was unable to move more than millimetres despite the incessant tense contraction of writhing muscles.

It would be impossible for any publisher to print what happened. The girls were vicious sadists but from the beginning Paula Stoicheva was in charge. Together they reduced their 'subject' to a quivering mass of tortured flesh. And in the end did the most dreadful thing of all when one of the women, a petulant-looking brunette, slipped a glass tube into one part of his body. The Stoicheva woman finished the act, crushing the flesh with her hands and causing the thin glass to grind into splinters which must have cut him in scores of unseen places.

The prisoner made hardly a sound. Only gurgling noises which were worse than any scream.

'Because,' explained Stoicheva, 'first he was beaten across the throat so that he would be silent.' A ball of wool packed with fine pins had then been thrust into his mouth and his lips were sealed with adhesive tape. If he moved the pins would prick his throat and tongue.

And at last he became limp when either death or unconsciousness ended the scene.

Stoicheva watched the trolley as the girls wheeled it from the room. 'That is what we did in Recsk,' she said. 'And then afterwards, we made love with the one who still lived.'

Hristo's voice sounded very tired. 'Now will you talk?'

The room was again warm. The lights had become more heavily crimson than before, so red, in fact, that the design of the carpet or paper on the farther side of the room could not be separated from the crimson fug. Stoicheva was lying on one of the chairs and the three of us were again alone.

But somewhere, I knew, there would be a tape or a mike. The golden pendulum of the clock still swayed against the wall and the sickening recurring swing of it had begun to jar. The endless click-clack, click-clack was like a sledge-hammer booming in my ears and the memory of the things I had seen was making me sick.

'For God's sake,' I said, 'let me sit for a minute and pull myself together. Leave me till I can think straight.'

'Talk,' said Hristo. 'There is no point in being brave when you can be sensible.'

The clock pointed at eleven-five. But I was too frightened even to make any calculation as to the real time although I knew that Trudie must be ending luncheon somewhere, if she was still in circulation. Dinner and the theatre could be only a few hours ahead. Without the seconal I would have been gibbering with fear. Not even a broad medical life which had shown horror in plenty could harden one against evil like the tortures of the Stoicheva woman.

She was standing by my side, chest heaving with emotion, eyes sparkling and lips glinting wet with saliva. Her fingers were still splashed with blood and her long thumbnail had been torn, the painted fragment hanging from the skin at one corner. Her hair was in disarray and her heavy lipstick had become smeared down over her chin.

Hristo was standing by her side, one hand on her right arm. He was pale and I thought that his voice was less steady.

'Do not be foolish, Doctor,' he said slowly. 'Paula has many tricks which she is still ready to use. She is a wild cat. But I know her well. Tell us what you know.'

'Or else?'

'You will be killed by the ladies. They were all trained by Commandant Piroshka and kill slowly. The man you saw will now be dead.'

'Why?'

'He was a traitor and said too much to the Turks.'

'But if I tell you everything I know about anti-matter or promise to do propaganda how can I be sure that you will let me go?'

'Because,' said Paula, 'we have also got your friend Hanna from Donauwörth. If you don't talk now she will die along with yourself and your wife will be killed later. But if you do talk and keep your promises to do some propaganda you shall get off with very little punishment.'

'Very little.'

'I told you that you interested me,' she grinned. 'You interest

35

me more now. It will be amusing to see how well you can make love when you say that you love only your wife.'

'Can I see Hanna?'

Hristo lifted one corner of the carpet. A heavy square of thick glass had been inlaid on to the floor. It covered part of a small room, almost a cell. Hanna was sitting on a wooden stool. She looked very tired and her lips were moving. And as I watched I remembered her stories of Ravensbrück, how, when she was afraid, she had tried to recite all the poetry of her childhood in order to remain sane.

'How did you get her?' I asked. My world seemed to have collapsed. So much sorrow sprung from foolish curiosity and an approach which lacked every refinement of technique!

'I know nothing about her except that she is your friend and one of the least important women in Donauwörth. Her disappearance will not interest the West German police. But it will keep you in order.'

The carpet flopped back into position. Stoicheva continued to stand beside the picture of her brother. The room was more heavily crimson than ever as the strip lighting glowed with rising intensity. It was again warm and Hristo returned to the divan. 'Well?'

My story had to be fool-proof. And the best way to make it fool-proof was to stick as much as possible to truth. I explained how the word anti-matter had meant nothing until I heard it mentioned at the American party: how I was curious to see two American security men talk with Serov: how I bluffed and the bluff worked: how I tried to wriggle out of a dangerous situation by some quick thinking about my aunt in Rutherglen: how my accidental meeting with one of the Americans at the Exhibition had convinced me that something important was in the air, and how I had spoken with everyone who might know anything during the winter.

'That we either knew or guessed,' said Hristo. 'Now tell us what you discovered.'

'Anti-matter is an advanced by-product of nuclear fission,' I explained slowly. 'The Americans and the British know how in theory to produce it but they believe that it can never be used.'

36

'Why?'

I was on dangerous ground but hoped for the best. 'Experiments were carried out in the States and also in Australia. Something went wrong and several people were killed. It is now believed that stuff called anti-matter could be developed, stuff which would literally destroy matter, destroy land even, but that if it were used there would be no way of restricting the effect of an explosion and chain reactions might literally annihilate the entire globe.'

'Who told you that?'

It was too dangerous to hesitate and I dived in head first. 'Everyone thinks that British Intelligence is M.I.5. But it is not. M.I.5 is only the fifth section of Military Intelligence and it is concerned with catching spies. Other more important branches deal with organization of security, winkling out the secrets of other countries and concealing matters of importance which the Government considers to be "against public interest". My brother Alistair sometimes assists a department which covers home secrets not for general consumption even within Britain. Alistair rarely lets his left hand know what his right hand is doing but from time to time if some matter of scientific or medical interest arises he may tell me a little.

'When I told him the story he filled in a few blanks. He knew enough to be sure that our top people have given up all idea of pursuing research into anti-matter.'

'And you have no other proof?' said Hristo.

'One other pointer. The Americans are trying hard to get a satellite which will be fixed in space like a permanent moon over any selected target. Technical difficulties make them believe that this will be impossible for at least ten years. They used to think that such a satellite loaded with anti-matter or some such other offensive weapon could be used either to stop war or else to win a war.'

'Used to?'

'Now they know that anti-matter is too dangerous.'

'How do you know?'

'One of your agents, comrades, brothers or cousins in Britain told me. Some of our political people are anti-American and wish

37

Britain to leave N.A.T.O. They also wish to deny bases to the Americans. The real reason is that a few of the top men in this group are scared in case American use of anti-matter goes wrong and Britain is erased from the seas.'

'But they told you that America had given up hope of developing it.'

'Sure. But they are still afraid something else may take its place. Already Americans have spoken about Britain as being one part of the world which is "expendable" in the event of nuclear war. These men don't want to be expended. They have good sources of information and Fred Hand* was perfectly frank. He said that the Americans had given anti-matter up. But that it was only a question of time till they got ideas about something else and his people weren't going to stop campaigning to have them pushed out of Britain and Western Europe.'

'What did the physicists say?'

The question seemed harmless but I remembered the agent who was said to know me and wondered. Vaguely I sensed that one of the physicists might be the man and stuck rigidly to fact. My wits were now working overtime and much of our conversation returned to mind. I told it all because none of it was terribly important. But if he was the Communist agent a single error in fact might bring me down.

Stoicheva and Hristo were equally alert and another man had also joined us, a short, stocky individual with a heavy moustache and sensitive fingers who sat opposite . . . staring unwinkingly at my face as I spoke.

I reported every word of these fragmentary conversations which I could remember and slowly the atmosphere began to relax until there was nothing left to say.

'You have forgotten nothing?' asked the newcomer. His voice was a soft, deep rumble.

'Nothing,' I agreed.

'What about your brother-in-law in Holland? You mentioned anti-matter to him at one stage. Did he know anything? He is, after all, legal adviser to the Dutch Government on matters affecting atomic power.'

* This is a pseudonym.

The knowledge of these people was terrifying. I had mentioned anti-matter to my friend and brother-in-law, Hans Mani. But he too had known nothing.

'How did you discover that?'

The newcomer smiled slowly and lit a cigarette fused with a Russian cardboard holder. 'He mentioned it to someone at a conference and we wondered.'

'Well I am sure that that is all,' I said. I was tired. So tired with reaction and drug that I wanted only to sleep. Even the horrifying business of torture had become almost a dream, and as I sat staring ahead at the pink wall the monotonous rhythm of that clicking clock and the sweep, backwards and forwards, backwards and forwards, of its shining golden pendulum was stealing my senses.

And then I was alone. I do not remember the others leaving the room. I only know that they went and that I was left to sit in that crimson room, alone, alone: alone; alone! Almost I could scream, then came a voice, a neutral, judicial, impartial, cold and aloof voice.

'Now tell me why you are going to Turkey?'

I replied almost automatically. One part of my brain remembered Kennedy and his thoughts about various approaches to hypnosis. I guessed that they were trying to put me under. I was even amused. It was so easy just to sit there and tell the truth. Why bother about silly things like hypnosis anyhow? Truth drugs and hypnosis were for paper-back thrillers. Truth drugs. Truth drugs. HYP-nosis. HYP-nosis. HYP-nosis. The swinging pendulum was part of it too! Sometimes they could use a swirling bowl of water. Sometimes a silver coin held in a hand. Sometimes a look was enough. HYP-nosis. Hyp-nosis. It was damn funny really to be kidnapped in Sofia and hypnotized in a crimson room. No one would ever believe it. No one. No one. No one. To hell with that clock. That CLOCK! That CLOCK!

Thinking back it seems a miracle that I managed to pull myself together. The set-up had almost worked. Time is always relative, even with faked clocks, and I dare say that all these thoughts swept through my remaining consciousness in a fraction of a second. But I realized in time that a new and much more subtle test lay ahead.

39

I knew also that they could not have expected me to go 'under' immediately and that a fractional delay in replying would be taken as reasonable.

'Why are you going to Turkey?' said the same voice again. Quiet, insistent and neutral.

'Because I wished to find out about developments along the Black Sea coast.' I knew, even if I was already almost half controlled, that only truth could now save me.

'How did you learn of them?'

'Kenneth de Courcy published something in an *Intelligence Digest*.'

'So you go to Turkey because of rumour in a war-mongering pamphlet?'

'I wondered if it tied up with anti-matter.'

'But you knew that anti-matter had been found dangerous. Too dangerous.'

'I wondered if the Russians had discovered a way round the danger.'

'Why?'

'Because they are clever people.'

'You knew nothing of anti-matter until the Americans spoke about it to Serov?'

'Nothing.'

'Why did you think that a word carried through a room during a drunken party was important?'

'Because I have a suspicious mind and I did not like the sound of that word.'

'What other reason made you go to Turkey?'

'I wished to see Istanbul.'

'Why did you write to the Turkish Foreign Minister Zorlu and ask to meet the country's leaders?'

'Because I needed good material for my Turkish lectures.'

'And why should British people be interested in Zorlu?'

'Because Menderes, the Prime Minister, crashed in an aeroplane near London. His name is now interesting to the British people and has a news value.'

The temperature of the room was rising even higher and my brow was dripping sweat. The pendulum was gleaming like burnished gold as some trick of light played within it : a wire down the shaft, I suspected, and connected with a light. The room was now wholly crimson and I remembered the old Chinese torture of imprisoning a man in a red chamber with no relief to his senses. But here there was relief : relief from gazing at a golden ball swinging to ... and ... fro ... To ... and ... fro ... To ... and ... fro.

Almost I had slipped away a second time. The voice recalled me at the crucial moment. 'There is no such thing as anti-matter. No such thing as anti-matter. You never heard of it. It does not exist. Repeat after me.'

I repeated.

'Say it again.'

'There is no such thing as anti-matter. I never heard of it. It does not exist.'

'NO one has heard of anti-matter. It does not exist. Repeat the words. It does not exist.'

And so it went on. Click-clack. The very monotony of it was hypnotic in itself. And then the voice changed.

'Do you love your wife?'

'Yes.'

'Do you want any other woman?'

'No.'

'Why? Are you inhuman?'

'I love my wife. I am not inhuman.'

'Do you wish Paula to be your mistress?'

'I do not.'

'Then as a test of your obedience to us you will do as she wishes when she returns. Repeat.'

Almost did I wish to vomit. My bowels seemed to have dropped through the floor and again I was terrified. It was an old, old trick. Make the man do something under hypnosis which is alien to him. If he does not do it he has not been hypnotized. He has been bluffing. It is the supreme test.

'I shall do as she wishes.' The words sounded thick and incoherent. But that was as it should have been. No one under hypnosis will do anything foreign to his nature without protest unless he has been given a good reason. I had been given a good reason.

'You will be returned to the hotel in time to meet your wife. But you will remember nothing. Repeat.'

'I shall remember nothing.'

'Stoicheva will return in a few minutes. When she has finished with you she will take you to a car. You will be driven back to the Balkan Palace. You will have forgotten everything. When your wife asks where you have been you will say that you went to Boyana. Paula will give you a brochure describing the paintings. You will read it and remember. You will then be able to answer every question you may be asked about Boyana. You had luncheon in a nearby hotel. You ate soup and *pilaf*. You had no coffee but you took a beer on the way home. Hristo was a perfect host. Repeat all that I have said.'

Again I repeated.

The voice became commanding. 'You will remember everything you have been told. When Stoicheva has finished with you she will return you to the car. Until then you will do as she wishes.'

The room was again lightening as the strip lamps paled to a pinkish lustre. Once more the carpet design came through and the clock faded to normal. The pendulum, once more, was a mottled piece of gilded glass and the clock dappled with dust.

The last words of the voice were concise. 'You will pick up the threads again when Stoicheva takes you to your car. Everything else will then be forgotten excepting Boyana, your lunch and your beer.'

*   *   *

The wall door opened once again and the woman arrived, smiling. One of the girls was behind her carrying a pot of tea. Two glasses were on the tray and a lemon had been sliced.

'Russian tea,' said Stoicheva. 'It is the best tea.'

As the girl laid things down and turned to go Stoicheva spoke quickly in another language. They glanced at the clock. It was only one-thirty. 'I was arranging when to fetch the car.' said the woman.

Once more she had changed. A sheer cocktail dress of dove-grey fitted her like a glove. Her torn nail had been trimmed and her make-up adjusted. Her hair was swept back in a severely boyish quiff and her eyes were once more smiling.

As she handed me the glass of tea she lifted my hand and kissed the pink burn which ran across the back. 'Sometimes I am too quickly angry,' she said. 'Soon I will repay.'

I dare say there are things in every life which should be forgotten, which men and women would pay a fortune to be able to forget. Stoicheva is still one of my nightmares.

Even as I write these words the memory of her salacious viciousness makes me writhe with anger. I tell the story only because it is an essential part of the record and to show how ruthless underground war can be. Because, make no mistake about it, this was war. One man had already died in that house and almost before my eyes.

And as she lingered with me I sensed that we were being watched, that a false expression or move on my part would be taken as a lie. The price of my life, the price of Trudie's life, the possibility of being able to follow this thing up was to accept a creature more evil than Messalina and more self-adoring than Nana.

*   *   *

In the end she relented. 'You will bathe and return to the car. I shall collect you in half an hour.'

Shortly after the clock pendulum had ceased to glow I had seen that it had returned to normal time-keeping. Now it was six-twenty and I was due to meet my wife at seven o'clock.

The plumbing in the house was good. The bathroom was sumptuous and even a cake of finely prepared bath-salts had been provided. The scent was pine needles. 'If you have been in Boyana's pine woods you will smell of them,' said Stoicheva. 'We like always to be thorough.'

Afterwards there was more coffee and we walked downstairs to the car. Hristo was driving and he spoke to me as though we had just left the monastery, discussing Byzantine art until the end of the journey. At the hotel a suave young man dressed in white ducks and a blue blazer opened the car door. Like all other staff members his English was good. 'Madame is waiting for you in the dining-room, sir. I told her that you may have been delayed on your return from the mountains.'

Hristo smiled broadly. 'We have all had a splendid day. It was lovely at Boyana and the paintings were magnificent.'

'The Doctor is tired,' said the receptionist. 'Would he care for an aperitif?'

Hristo made his only joke of the day. 'He has already had too much aperitif. I think it is food now.'

Trudie was waiting for me in the dining-room with two members of Bulgarian P.E.N. who had called to discuss poetry and other literary subjects. Our host at the opera concert was also in the offing and begging me to rush dinner in case we should be late for the show.

The concert was superb. Indeed it remains one of the finest performances of folk music to which I have ever listened. A choir from Varna was best of all and at one point sang the famous 'Echo Song'. I shall always believe that it restored my sanity.

In the hotel I spoke at length of our wonderful day. Trudie knew that the room might be wired and that I was only putting on a show. Nor was it possible to write. There were too many potential peep-holes in the elaborately carved ceiling for that. Nor did we even dare to speak in our own car. Short-wave transmission mikes can be concealed almost in a walnut and even the car was not safe.

We ventured to say a little only in the bathroom, and then in a whisper whilst both taps were turned fully on. And enough was said only to make her understand the need for playing a part until the frontier . . . and Turkey.

5

The coast of fear

I WAS worried about Hanna although I did not believe that she was hostage against my own good behaviour. That was an obvious red herring. I had been given hypnotic suggestion which was supposed to have 'worked' and my acting must have been convincing or else we would not have left the country. So far as they were concerned the hypnosis had been successful and I should have forgotten Hanna, forgotten the tortures of a young man and forgotten much that I knew of even Paula Stoicheva. I must, there-fore, carry on through Turkey according to our prearranged schedule.

There were many reasons why Hanna might have been kid-napped. She lived dangerously and could have become suspect for many reasons. If so Hans, her husband, might also be in trouble. He might even be dead, and the more I thought of it the more convinced I became that nothing we could do would affect Hanna in any way. She had been used impulsively as a threat and could not otherwise influence the pattern of events.

Even so I was anxious to contact Hans and get him up to date. In the end I wrote a letter home, gave it to the captain of a British ship in Istanbul and asked him to post it in Piraeus on the following day. It was addressed to my brother, who would put two and two together, contact Hans and leave it to him to do what he could.

After that the wisest thing was to follow our programme. A trip along the Black Sea coast had earlier been arranged and for a week we played the tourist.

It was a wonderful journey, the *Akdeniz* calling at nine or ten delightful townships between Istanbul and the Soviet frontier. Indeed it was such a fascinating trip that I did a broadcast some time later to plug the area as a new tourist attraction. It went out over the Home Service and influenced at least a few families during the following summer.

But the ship also held a mixed bag of odd people, some of them Americans off to N.A.T.O. bases along the northern coast of Asia Minor. One or two were interesting. Most of them seemed unhappy and a few of the younger men were frankly scared.

'It's this goddam business at Trabzon,' said one man returning from home leave. 'The Russians have got a fancy radar beam which sometimes lures our boys off path. A few have drifted over Soviet territory and then been shot down. Makes the boys edgy.'

Another man was more explicit. 'That ain't what's getting our Government down,' he said morosely. 'There's something cooking across the frontier which none of us just don't nohow understand.'

'Such as?'

He was long-winded about it but the story boiled down to this: patrolling aircraft took regular daily or weekly photographs of the Soviet frontier and of parts inland. All fixed landmarks had been well pin-pointed and it had long been impossible for any troop movements, military installation or anything else to take place without registering on miles of ciné film.

'So?' I asked as the Major hesitated.

'Recently one of the boys made a routine repeat sortie deep inside the U.S.S.R. He nailed good pix and now they say he was off course.'

'Who says?'

'Our O.C. and the security boys.'

'Why?'

'Seems that if he was where he says he was something must have happened to a couple of biggish hills.'

'How?'

'They ain't there.'

'How come?'

'Listen, boy,' said the Major. 'We know every pimple in

46

Western Russia, even far down south and a helluva lot of other bits as well. O.K. One week there are some hills. Next week there's no hills. O.K. So the guy who took the pix wasn't there or else the Russians have moved a couple of fair-sized landmarks without using even a bulldozer.'

'Well then the pilot was off course.'

The Major smiled sarcastically. 'Tell Hank that and then get ready to run. That boy is good. If he says he was there then he was there. And if he took his pix there then the Russkies have rubbed out a couple of hills overnight.'

'Perhaps the Batum beam affair put him off,' I suggested. 'After all, several experienced pilots have been tricked over Russia and shot down.'

This wasn't near Batum and anyhow Hank was flying with several new navigational devices thought up to beat the murder beam.

'All right, soldier,' I said. 'Facts are facts. So the Russians removed two hills overnight. How did they do it?'

The men looked at one another seriously. 'That is the sixty-four thousand dollar question,' said the Major.

The Colonel was a slow-spoken man from Texas, tall, gaunt and imperturbable. 'Ah jes' refuse t'believe t'implications.'

'What implications?' I asked.

'There jes' ain't no sech animile as a guy that can remove mountains overnight. Hank was sure off course.'

'Well then, Colonel,' I said, 'why are you all so scared?'

It was a tactless question, but no one knew the answer. In the end everything was left vaguely uncertain, but enough had happened to make everyone in the area nervous. The rumour of new missile sites on the northern Black Sea coast-line was bad enough. Some of them were said to be loaded and prepared to blast the Middle East to smithereens on a phone call from Moscow. Others were poised to strike across the Balkans into Western Europe. One at least was said to be capable of reaching the United States itself.

Occasionally unexplained air catastrophes suggested some murder weapon used to bring down even unarmed aircraft. Others believed that N.A.T.O. planes were deliberately lured over the Soviet frontier to create 'incidents' and no one knew who would be next to fall for a bluff which seemed unanswerable.

But the mystery of the disappearing hills worried the Colonel more than anything else and his conclusions were sober.

'Somethin's agoin' on which strikes at the very heart of matter itself: 'tain't surprisin' our boys are scared.'

But on that point we got little change out of the Turks. There was a good deal of anti-American feeling during the summer of 1959 and the average Turk believed that 'Americans see a shadow on every wall'.

They themselves were more interested in the Menderes Press Laws, suppression of free speech and the general iniquity of the régime to be bothered about anything else, and in any case Namil Gedik's National Police had made criticism of anything a dangerous pastime.

Even so we returned to Istanbul. Enough had been discovered to tie up with our suspicions and we guessed that Russia was on to something big. I had also begun to wonder about the Democrats and Prime Minister Menderes. Soviet or Rumanian ships were now calling at Stamboul on alleged 'Black Sea – Marmora' cruises and few of the passengers seemed bona-fide travellers. I also remembered the curiosity of my unseen inquisitor in Sofia. 'Why are you going to Turkey?' And the blunt remark, 'He said too much to the Turks.'

Why did he wish to know? What had that poor tortured prisoner said?

Was it possible that the Democrats were preparing to sell out of N.A.T.O. to the U.S.S.R.?

And then I remembered Mr. Pulliam, editor of the *Arizona Republic* and *Indianapolis Star*. Not long ago he had stated that if Prime Minister Menderes did not change his policy the Western position in Turkey might become untenable. What had he implied? Did Mr. Pulliam know about anti-matter, I wondered, or did he simply mean that Democrat corruption in Turkey would undermine N.A.T.O. security?

I decided to find out.

Zorlu, the Foreign Minister, had already been approached for interview.

He proved an elusive subject, however, and at first we saw Ismail Soysal, the official public relations officer in Ankara.

Mr. Soysal was polite but formal and said little.

A few weeks later, after our second return to Istanbul, Zorlu made a swift visit to the Hilton Hotel to discuss certain matters with Sir Campbell Stuart, a director of *The Times*. Namik Gedik, the Minister of the Interior, was also in Istanbul, probably coping with security arrangements, and an interview was arranged with a man who, even at that time, was the most feared Minister in Turkey.

Zorlu was a sleek careerist and opportunist who lacked much of the fire and ability of ex-President Celal Bayar or Adnan Menderes, but he was a master hand at saying nothing and in clouding any issue with a fog of words. Gedik, on the other hand, said little to strangers at any time and his silence was more sinister than I cared to admit. At last I became impatient and tried to force the pace. 'Listen, sir. Why does Turkey allow phoney Soviet or Rumanian cruise ships to call at Istanbul? I don't believe that one passenger in six is on holiday. They remind me of Hitler's scouts in every European holiday centre before the war. All busy photographing things which might be useful, planning billets for troops and establishing contact with their fifth column.'

The question raised a storm. Turkey nourished friendly relations with all people including the U.S.S.R. She could not deny berths to the pleasure ships of Rumania or Russia. What was I suggesting?

'That these Communist visitors are here on business. And it is business which will not help either N.A.T.O. or the Turkish people.'

He was angry now. But still cautious. He did not like my suggestions and demanded explanations. Was I suggesting that Turkey would fail to honour her N.A.T.O. obligations?

'No, sir,' I said. 'But when I find obvious Communist agents coming ashore with brief-cases and meeting directors of some of your key banks or industries, failing to do the ordinary tourist round, and taking pictures with tele-lenses of your barracks, military installations along the Bosphorus and airfields, I am entitled to wonder why your Government permits it.'

49

He became more angry than ever and his normally pale lips drew into a thin white line. 'This interview is now over.'

I tried one more shot. 'Are you doing a deal with anti-matter?'

Although I had become accustomed to bluff this was the most effective to date. Gedik's face flushed with rage. His eyes sparkled with temper and he called one of his secretaries.

I tried to bluff further. 'Listen, sir, in my profession, or rather in my several professions of doctor, traveller, lecturer, and so forth, I meet many people. You know that there is opposition in Turkey to your Government. You also know that anti-matter exists and that the Russians are developing it. We, in the West, your allies under N.A.T.O., are anxious about defects in Turkish security. We do not like to see Soviet ships sailing so close to bases on your territory. We have experience of fifth columns and we do not like to see Communists establishing relationships with key men, or certain key men, in a country upon which our whole Middle Eastern defence position rests.'

For a second or two the Minister hesitated and then he dismissed his secretary. 'What else do you wish to say? Can you explain why Turkey should have confidence in N.A.T.O. when none of her allies has got this new weapon but when she knows that the Soviet Union has almost perfected it?'

I was almost shivering with relief. Proof at last! But not proof which would satisfy a jury.

'Tell me, sir. Why do you think Britain is so reluctant to engage in a space programme or in making costly ballistic missiles? Do you honestly believe that it is British policy to remain defenceless?'

'Britain has been declining.'

'How many nations have thought that and lived to regret it? Germany thought we were declining and where is Ribbentrop now?'

He was becoming interested and I continued to bluff to the limit. 'I can tell you, sir, that Britain is not interested in these things only because she is already so far advanced with her own new anti-matter weapon, which has been called A.M.1. With that behind her Turkey has no reason to fear anyone.'

'I am Minister of the Interior in a N.A.T.O. state. Why have I not been told of this?'

50

'Few people have been told of it. Do the Americans or Russians go around telling everyone of their most important advances?'

'Then why am I being told now and in this unorthodox fashion?'

'I have no authority to tell you anything and I may get into trouble for having done so. I told you only because I love Turkey and do not wish her to make the mistake of going red.'

For some time he sat quietly in his deep, easy chair. He was chewing a morsel of *Lokum** and his restless fingers fidgeted with the tassel of a cushion. 'The Soviet Union has gone far in this new field.'

'How far?' I asked.

He shook his head. 'I cannot say but our information suggests that the U.S.S.R. is likely soon to control the whole world . . . including China.'

'Because of this new weapon? The thing we British have called A.M.1.?'

'Because of that or something very like it. If Turkey is to survive she must deal with the strongest side.'

'So long as you remain in N.A.T.O. Turkey will be doing that.'

'Russia would like to see us out of N.A.T.O.'

'Well then, do as you please, but remember that if you desert Britain and America you are backing the wrong horse.'

'You assure me that Britain has this new weapon?' His voice was hard and formal.

'I do.'

'That with it she can defeat any combination of nations?'

'No. Not alone. But with N.A.T.O. assistance she could jointly defeat any combination.'

'You consider that Britain is further ahead than Russia with this new weapon?'

'Definitely, sir.'

'And what does Britain expect to do? How can I stop Soviet or any other ships from calling at Istanbul? It is an international touring centre.'

'Your own department can prevent bogus tourists from dealing with important officials and laying a Communist fifth column.'

Turkish delight.

51

We parted a few moments later. He was still suspicious. But we were mutually suspicious, so we cut even.

Turkey was then practically on the brink of either civil war or revolution and required only a good going spark to ignite everything. In the event nothing happened for almost eight more months, but I had not forgotten the Iraq revolt or the part played in it by Russia. Nor could I forget the events of only a few weeks earlier in Sofia and that one cold question: 'Why are you going to Turkey?'

I was now certain that a conspiracy existed to queer the N.A.T.O. pitch in Asia Minor and to eliminate one more free country in the Middle East. Moreover we had gone far towards proving that anti-matter did exist and was a probable danger of incalculable importance.

6

Underground in Istanbul

ISTANBUL is a city of many moods. Divided like Gaul into three parts each has its own character, its own personality and its own charm. And each is separated from the others by water. The Golden Horn cuts inland from the western end of the Bosphorus and its only two bridges unite old Stamboul with sprawling Pera and Beyoglu whilst the Bosphorus and narrowing end of Marmara separate both from Usküdar and the Asiatic shore.

Galata is the most romantic bridge in Europe. Sultans and grand viziers, concubines, eunuchs, soldiers and slaves alike have all paused in their crossing to savour the magnificent skyline and to gaze across blue waters towards Asia. Some of Turkey's most hated men were hanged from its arches and it has probably seen more picturesque drama than even Pont Neuf or Westminster, Avignon or Rialto. Today drama and glamour are less evident but Galata is still loved even by dangerous men, conspirators and traitors alike. Because Stamboul remains the favourite haunt of political idealists and Beyoglu is still a meeting-place for politicians and diplomats, news hawks and conferences.

During the late summer of 1959 Stamboul was seething with discontent and with National Police prowling the pavements from Beyazit to Topkapi and from the Fortress of the Seven Towers to Atatürk Boulevard. The University occupied most of their attention but little went on in any of the tea-houses or restaurants without its being reported.

Even students spoke in whispers and our meeting with friends was arranged for the Blue Mosque, where we could sit in privacy below the vast dome remote from eavesdroppers.

53

Orhan was nineteen and an idealist. He was in third-year law and for his age an expert on the Turkish Constitution. Cemil, his friend, was specializing in commercial law whilst Yildiz and her brother Turan were in the diplomatic service.*

They listened whilst I gave them a carefully censored version of our opinions. Nothing was said about anti-matter or any other new weapon and it was enough to argue the significance of visiting Communist ships, to suggest that they attach themselves as 'guides' to parties going ashore and see what happened. We threw out hints about a possible Turko–Soviet *rapprochement* and suggested the possibility of Turkey leaving N.A.T.O. In particular we asked that they sound the opposition Press, army cadets and Republican delegates to discover how the Government might be overthrown in the event of treachery.

Orhan Bey was a serious youth with an engaging manner. Like most Turks he also hated Communism and the new Russian Imperialism.

'The Press Laws make it impossible to print any criticism about Menderes's policy,' he said.

'But you know many opposition journalists and you can discover if they suspect a double-cross.'

Yildiz, being a woman, was perhaps more sensitive. 'Of course Turkey is being double-crossed. We all know that. But we don't know why. Is the Menderes crowd content with swindling us out of money or are they preparing a deal with Russia? Are they working for both sides or are they just stupid people playing with fire?'

'What sort of fire?' asked Trudie.

'American aid in goods is being distributed to party members as a reward for services, but it is really buying votes. Immense sums of money have been squandered in putting down new factories in the heart of Republican areas whether the factories are well sited or not. And again that is to try and buy votes from the opposition. Every journalist who criticizes either the character of our leaders or the policies they follow lands in jail. Hundreds are there already

---

* At the special insistence of our Turkish friends these names are pseudonyms. At the moment of writing it is still not wise for them to admit the part they played in events leading to the revolt of 27 May 1960.

and many without even a trial, because as you yourself know, a man can stay in a Turkish jail for months or even years before his case is heard in the courts. That could be bad government, but it is also playing with fire, and it is a fire which might lead to revolution although it is not pleasant to believe that Turkish leaders would ever make a pact with Russia or let down their Allies.'

'I don't suggest it,' I said slowly, and knowing the sensitive mood of our friends. 'I only wonder if it is possible.'

'Turks may be bad but they are never traitors,' said Turan with violence. 'They will not give salt to Russia.'

Whilst we were speaking one more contingent of Soviet tourists arrived to see the mosque. A woman sat down heavily upon a fragile table, which broke into smithereens. The party laughed and another kicked the pieces with his foot.

An elderly Imam, teaching children in a quiet corner, looked across. His eyes were calm but his knuckles blenched white as he gripped the Koran. His children watched the Soviet tourists politely and then one of them padded quietly away. Trudie also rose and walked round the walls towards the door, slipped on her shoes again and sauntered into the courtyard.

She returned a few moments later, laughing. 'He had a little knife,' she explained, 'and now there are eight punctured Soviet wheels. A man tried to catch him but the last I saw the boy was tearing along the Hippodrome towards Aya Sophya.'

'See what I mean,' said Turan. 'Even the children are anti-Russian.'

'Unfortunately our political leaders are not children,' said Cemil. 'I agree with Trudie and George. Celal Bayar is a bad man. He was not so bad until 1954 or so, but since then he has been bad. He worships money and could be bribed. The Americans have also said that unless "aid" is supervised they will not go on pumping dollars into private pockets. Menderes is too ambitious. Now he is not content with being Prime Minister of Turkey and may have ideas about leading a coalition in the Middle East. Zorlu is a fool and weak. He will do as he is told and his wife is extravagant. They also need money and he could be bribed. Gedik is bad and he is both ambitious and dangerous.'

55

'How do you know all this?' asked Yildiz. 'Madame Zorlu can be charming.'

'Any woman can be charming if her husband has enough money,' said Cemil. 'Madame Zorlu's husband spends more than he can honestly earn.'

'But how do you know?' Yildiz persisted.

'My work takes me into big business houses. My chiefs advise on projected new deals. My immediate superior often gives a legal opinion about things which may be near the bone and when I look back upon the situation as a whole I believe there could be misuse of public funds.'

The conversation became general, but it was enough to have interested the students and got them started on a mission which suited their temperament. All were strongly anti-Menderes and anti-Democrat. All hated the Minister of the Interior. All longed for free elections and they were all capable. In a few months at the most they would have a clear picture of everything which mattered.

Yildiz was the first to go. 'Summing up,' she said, 'you want us to check up on phoney Communist tourists, to see if the newsmen suspect a Soviet pact, secret or otherwise, and to discover the extent of political corruption. Right?'

'And also to discover what can be done about it if our suspicions are proven,' I added.

In the light of experience, communications might be dangerous so we arranged that letters would normally be sent through the captain of a Turkish ship who could be trusted. They would then be posted in either Piraeus or Marseilles and replies would be sent to an address in Holland where they would be redirected to a poste restante in Italy for collection by our captain friend.

A simple code for direct use was also arranged based upon British nursery rhymes, since the students spoke fluent English, having been educated at Robert College, Istanbul.

For example 'Humpty Dumpty had a great fall' would mean that evidence of serious political corruption had been proven.

'Little Jack Horner sat in a corner' meant that preparations would be made to overthrow the Government.

'All the King's horses and all the King's men couldn't put

Humpty together again' showed that plans were advanced for action.

'Mary had a little lamb, its fleece was white as snow' indicated that Menderes and company had been investigated and found reliable so far as N.A.T.O. was concerned.

'One, two, buckle my shoe' could be used to indicate dates.

'Polly put the kettle on' was a case for urgent help.

'Old Mother Hubbard' would be used if the cupboard were bare and the students needed weapons.

'There was an old woman lived in a shoe' meant that there were large numbers of people involved in some major political intrigue involving alliance with the U.S.S.R.

'Ride a cock horse to Banbury Cross' was an invitation to go out to Turkey as soon as possible.

Finally 'Hickory dickory dock' would be used only to show that something immensely serious had been discovered and that British or American agents must establish contact with Yildiz at once.

We also promised the students that no foreigners would interfere without permission in anything which might develop. Turkey, they explained, was well able to solve her own problems without outside assistance.

We left the mosque in dribs and drabs, Trudie with Yildiz going ahead for tea at the Divan Hotel, the students returning to classes at the New University and myself to wander at leisure through the bazaar to Galata and a Dolmus taxi.

A few days later we sailed on the *Ankara* for Marseilles and a swift run home.

Only one incident can be reported during the return trip. I put a phone call through to Donauwörth from Grenoble. Hans was at home and sounded tired. It was at least an even chance that his line was tapped, and one had to be careful.

'*Ja.*'

'Burns speaking,' I said. Hans sometimes said that he had only two Scottish friends, the poet Burns and myself.

'*Ja.* Did you have a good trip?'

'So-so. But there was trouble in fixing terms. They did not like our contract.'

'Did you talk with the management?'

'I saw two or three of the partners who seemed authorized to do business but they were not interested in anything we had to sell. Not enough profit perhaps.'

'We are making little enough profit ourselves. Everywhere you go prices are high.'

'Did you get my letter asking for advice?'

'*Ja*. But I was not surprised. Other people were there before you and got in first.'

'One of them is an odd sort of person who was reciting poetry when I last saw them.'

'Ach yes,' laughed Hans jovially. 'That means they have not pulled the deal off. Some of us whistle if a deal goes wrong. Others go and get drunk. But that one says poetry. It is all very silly. Did you not take heart and try to win the contract after all?'

'I think our customers will go elsewhere. They don't seem to like our goods. I couldn't interest them.'

'Well, send your expense account in just the same, Mr. Burns. You did your best and if they don't like our product what does it matter? Some are for, some are anti.'

'It's the antis that cause trouble, sir,' I said. 'Sorry I couldn't get a contract but better luck to us both next time.'

'There will be no next time with that firm,' said Hans. 'The present tender has already cost us too much and I don't think we'll get our money back.'

'No point in starting all over again,' I agreed.

'Not there at any rate,' said Hans. 'But I will see what else the market offers and get in touch with you.'

'You have no other contracts in mind? I may go off for that leave you promised?'

'And have a good time.'

He hung up abruptly and I turned to Trudie, who had been taking every word down in her strictly personal mixture of Dutch shorthand and abbreviated English. 'Let's get that lot deciphered and see what we can make of it.'

Our interpretation of the news was bad. Hanna had got on to something before ourselves and had rushed into the Balkans on a mission. Hans did not expect to see her again. He himself was preparing to move and would contact me only after he had changed his identity and built up a front elsewhere.

*   *   *

In a story of this sort it is difficult to tie up loose ends in dramatic sequence within the last few pages. And in any case this is not a spy novel or a detective thriller. Many loose ends remain to be tied even in 1961 and Hanna is still missing.

Hans says that she had unearthed evidence relating to the whereabouts of two female wardens from Ravensbrück who are still wanted by the German courts. The chase led her to Greece and foolishly she decided to go by car. He last heard of her in Yugoslavia and believes that she must have been arrested somewhere in Bulgaria.

There is also reason to believe that Sofia has a police headquarters disguised as a government office or block of flats and that it is used only for the interrogation of political prisoners. The Commandant is said to be a woman and several of her staff were trained at Recsk.

Recsk, let it be understood, is the notorious A.V.O. (Secret Police) prison sixty miles or so north-east of Budapest where discipline is ruthless and only the most sadistic guards have lately been employed. There are endless stories of its cruelties which rival even those of Belsen or Dachau, and those few men whom I have met and who have survived imprisonment at Recsk were scarred physically and mentally for life.

None were expected to escape, but after the Hungarian revolt some did reach Austria and their tales rank amongst the most beastly obscenities of recorded history. The woman Piroshka is an expert in torture employed by the A.V.O. for special missions and was finally appointed Commandant at the worst camp of all.

Her years in Recsk mark the most diabolical period of Hungarian history. Many of her staff who now serve the Russians formerly served Horthy and Hitler. But under her discipline the former Hungarian Secret Police organization—which in the old days was almost respectable—has become equal in viciousness to anything ever known to Russia's O.G.P.U. and Yagoda.

The woman herself is short and rather plump. She was once

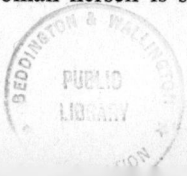

pointed out to me in the foyer of Budapest's Margitziget Hotel and I remember her chiefly because of her pock-marked face and bad dress sense. At best her clothes were in poor taste, fussy and blatantly cut to reveal a figure which had begun to sag.

She was with two other women, younger than herself, and a youth whom someone said was her son.

At that time the name Recsk meant only one more concentration camp and the Continent was full of camps and of men or women who had worked in camps. But now that I know more of Recsk and have seen the work of her pupils I wish that I had paid more attention to a creature who, in the words of one man, 'is a creature God vomited, but who is so dirty that not even the Devil will sweep her up'.

7

Piecing the jigsaw

THE winter of 1959–60 passed for myself in a haze of perplexity which did not break until early 1960 and then events marched so quickly that even now I feel that I have never managed fully to catch up with them. But first it was essential to assess the situation, and I find that it always helps at such times to write things down. My list of facts eventually made stimulating reading.

The Soviet Foreign Minister had virtually admitted fore-knowledge of the Iraq revolt. Whether or not he had realized the fate in store for the royal family was a moot point but the chances were that he could have expected nothing else.

On the basis of this and considering the rest of my conversation with Gromyko, the Soviet New Look of friendship was false.

This premise was supported by any study of up-to-date Communist doctrinaire writings, all of which insisted that the Soviet Government had not deviated in any way from basic Marxism.

One salient point in the Marxist thesis is that Communism must establish world domination only through war or revolution and it seemed that preparations for both might well be afoot.

General Serov had now been demoted but his department continued to function and its activities were made less evident only because of the over-riding need to maintain the New Look in order to lull capitalist governments into a sense of false security.

The Russian Secret Police had established some sort of contact with at least two American security officials whose behaviour was open to suspicion so far as I was concerned, but who seemed, nevertheless, to be trusted by people who mattered.

The Menderes administration in Turkey might be contemplating a Soviet pact and might be preparing to leave N.A.T.O. despite promises to the contrary. Gedik in particular was worth watching.

Americans posted at Turkish Black Sea and other N.A.T.O. bases believed that a Russian secret weapon of unbelievable potential was in an advanced state of preparation.

There was reason to believe that substantial landmarks had been removed almost overnight in Russia without evidence as to how this had been done.

There was no doubt in my own mind that some by-product of nuclear fission did exist which had been called anti-matter, that the Russians were familiar with it, that it was known to at least the two American security men and that even certain Turkish officials had knowledge of its potential, and indeed may even have been scared into contemplating a Soviet alliance in order to save themselves from possible annihilation.

This weapon had been hinted at by Kenneth de Courcy in an earlier edition of *Intelligence Digest*, a news sheet internationally recognized as being far in advance of any other in winkling out knowledge of important secrets.

My German friend, Hans, had memories of the word anti-matter being used fifteen years earlier by a responsible physicist. Fifteen years is a long time in these days of scientific progress and something might well have come of it by now.

My own contacts in Britain had admitted vague knowledge of theoretical developments in nuclear fission which pointed to the possibility of complete destruction of physical matter, but had been unable to say how far development had progressed in either Britain or America.

My own experiences in Sofia confirmed that anti-matter was regarded as important by Russia. But I was still baffled as to why I had been allowed to leave the place at all. Either my own acting had been unusually good, my inquisitors had had unusual confidence in the power of hypnotic suggestion or else they may have thought that I was too unimportant to make the subject of an international incident which could have tarnished the New Look of friendship towards the Free World. But the main thing was that I had got away with it and for that must for ever remain grateful to Providence. It had been a narrow squeak.

But when all had been written and analysed it occurred to me that a number of important trends had also lately become evident and that they began to make sense only when one considered the possibility of some such new weapon being early available to the Russians . . . and possibly also to the Americans.

Perhaps most important of all was Khruschev's off-the-cuff remark to some Americans that 'he could bury them'.

Or his later statement to the Supreme Soviet that Russia now had weapons of such power as to be literally incredible.

And then again, why this Soviet-American preoccupation with luniks and satellites which seemed to fly lower and lower? There had even been one press reference to a satellite which might become a fixed artificial moon in any pre-determined spot. Hans had also hinted at much the same idea.

What, I asked myself, if that pre-determined spot were to be over the middle of the American continent and if the satellite were to contain some horror which could destroy a whole nation? Was that, perhaps, what Khruschev had implied when he said that he could bury America?

Everything, for some months, remained in the realms of pure speculation, but I also devoted myself seriously to a concentrated study of various scientific journals.

Medical training, together with researches into my own special subject, had accustomed me to the technique of using a reference library and combing the world's literature. Even so the task was immense, especially since I was ill-equipped to assess what might be significant. Indeed I might never have been able to light upon the things which mattered had it not been for the fact that *I did know something must exist*, that it had almost certainly arisen from some aspect of nuclear fission and that probably it had been earlier regarded as of purely theoretical significance.

I did have a hint that the Americans were 'on to it' but I was more impressed by the probability that Russia had overcome technical difficulties and devised methods of controlling some sort of entirely new physical force. Buoyed up with this assurance I then plodded my weary way through the journals. Much of the language was incomprehensible, but at last a pattern began to emerge. Reduced to its ultimate simplicity it seemed that certain basic facts pointed the direction of current research and that arising from this came the one thing which seemed to matter.

Again I tried to boil things down to a written list of first essentials.

Certain factors determine the destructive capacity of an atomic bomb and there is a fixed limit to its function as an offensive weapon.

A hydrogen bomb has no such limitations and there is no end-point to its destructive capacity.

If, however, an atomic bomb is surrounded by magnetic fields of sufficient strength and the whole built within a vacuum casing it was suggested that in theory no explosion would follow so long as the magnetic fields and vacuum were maintained. If either were removed, however, it seems that a new type of energy could be released which might 'theoretically' eliminate all physical matter in its path.

Bearing this in mind it seemed appropriate to call this destructive force anti-matter.

As I wrote these words for the first time during early 1960 it seemed that here might be a solution to the mystery of the missing hills in south-western Russia. Such energy might also be inter-reted as a weapon of incredible power which could 'bury America'.

Nor did it take long to realize that a permanent artificial moon a hundred or so miles above the earth and loaded with such a weapon which could be controlled from any point on the earth's surface would create a final threat to the very physical existence of a nation. Was this, I wondered, the real reason for this sputnik race to ruin upon which both sides seemed to be engaged? Was all the current talk of putting a man into space purely a red-herring to justify other activities? Or did the two end-points march hand in hand? Could a man in space perhaps be an essential part in the control of such a weapon?

Much remained in the realm of speculation but I decided to make certain assumptions which seemed reasonable to myself in the light of recent experience. The list was the shortest to date.

The Russians possessed a new weapon probably capable of destroying masses of land.

The present Soviet Government was still committed to world domination through war, revolution or both.

Time no longer lay on their side. It seemed that the optimum moment for starting global war would be mid-1960.

At this stage life then took one more unexpected twist when it became necessary to discuss the sale of certain photographs in Paris. The trip was a welcome break after weeks of wading through reference books and I looked forward to three days of good company and relaxation. Instead I found myself involved in a situation more off-beat than any to date.

I had decided on my first evening to visit Pigalle and try my luck with coloured photographs of the more interesting 'lights'. My tripod was set up at a street corner and I was focusing on the gaudy entrance to a night-club when a voice startled me.

'Damn silly taking pictures like that. I hate this place.'

The man was in early middle age and apparently respectable.

'What's wrong with it?' I asked.

His reply boiled down to 'everything'. He was English and lonely. He did not like Paris and had visited it for the first time only to have a 'bit of a fling' before going 'out into the blue'.

My own work was finished. Much of the evening remained free and I was interested in the fellow. 'Well, come and have a coffee and you can tell me which bit of the blue you are going to.'

He seemed glad to join me and we found a place in a crowded restaurant opposite the métro station.

'Which bit of the blue?' I repeated after we had given our order.

His reply was the last thing I could have expected. 'I'm off to Woomera to test our Blue Streak Rocket.'

Even so I managed to force a joke. 'Into the blue to fire a blue.'

'More or less,' he agreed.

'So this is a last binge before the Australian outback.'

''sright.'

'Is it any use?' I asked. 'After all, as a tax-payer I have an interest in the thing.'

He replied without hesitation. 'Terrific.'

'Range?'

He answered this and every other question with a blatant facility and disregard for security which made me shudder. Initial velocity, heat-resisting devices, fuel, trajectory, nose cones, parabolic curve and a deal of other professional jargon tripped from his lips in a non-stop stream which had to be heard to be believed.

In the end I set out to pump him dry. He answered every question and seemed completely taken aback when I turned upon him.

'You allow yourself to be picked up by a complete stranger in Pigalle of all places. You sit in a busy public café and babble top-secret information about one of Britain's most important weapons. You have been vetted and were accepted as a good security risk. What on earth have you got to say for yourself?'

He looked at me sullenly. 'Who are you?'

I hope that he reads this book and will then understand my reply, even if he did not do so at the time. 'Never mind that,' I bluffed. 'Just remember this. You talk too much. We have known for a while that you were a good technician. But we also know your weaknesses. You like to be a big man, to show off. Well, this is your last chance and you can take it as a final warning. If you open your mouth again to anyone you will be fired.'

Without saying more I rose and walked away.

The incident bordered upon the ridiculous and yet it had happened. The man had even given his name. He had claimed to be in charge of one particular and important aspect of the Blue Streak Rocket project. If he had spoken so freely to myself what might he have said to others?

The Paris trip had gone sour and I returned a day early to speak to the one man I knew who might be interested and know how to handle the situation.

Mr. Bernard Newman is Britain's leading authority on counter-espionage. He was coming to Scotland to give a few lectures and was due to stay with us for a night. I wanted more than anything else to ask him about anti-matter and to tell him of the talkative

66

Blue Streak Rocket engineer. There had been no witnesses to our conversation but I knew it had to be reported to someone.

A great deal of nonsense has been spoken and written about espionage in general and many people forget that the essence of all security work is secrecy. When a man or woman is known to be a spy he ceases to be useful. He therefore ceases to be a spy. Nor is it easy for an outsider to contact those authorities which do control the nation's security. Indeed it is probable that the outsider himself may then become an object of suspicion.

Bernard Newman appreciates the realities of spying more than any other person alive and I told him the whole Paris story, including the name of the man. He agreed that I could have handled the situation in no other way. We then turned to the question of anti-matter.

I did not expect him to say much even if he did know about weapons still on the secret list and hoped at best only to assess his reaction, but I did know that anything relevant would, in due course, percolate through to headquarters.*

The subject of his lectures was 'Russia' and it provided a suitable opening but I soon realized that I would get no change out of him. Anti-matter seemed to be news. But whether or not he was up to date in recent developments remained a mystery. Which was as it should have been under the circumstances. I did know, however, that if he considered the subject important my speculations would reach the people who mattered without delay.

A few weeks later Hans delivered one more unexpected bombshell in the jumble of facts during a rush visit to Britain early in the spring of 1960 and made because of very peculiar circumstances. His story was fascinating.

'You know Erich Mielke?' he said.

'By name only.'

'You are fortunate. I know him personally and hate every square inch of his squat little body. He is Germany's leading Communist. He was even a Communist in Hitler's Germany and joined the party when only fifteen.'

* Production of the Blue Streak Rocket ceased a few months later, and despite official reasons given for this I believe that my talkative Paris contact gave vital information to Soviet agents which nullified the use of our weapon.

'Nowadays you've got to be older. They must have been desperate for members.'

'They were,' said Hans. 'But Mielke has done well. Now he is East Germany's Minister of State Security. Pre-war warrants for his arrest on murder charges still hold good in Free Germany but he escaped in Hitler's day, reached Russia via Belgium and by 1945 was in charge of those Party Terror Squads which made Berliners feel that peace was more dangerous than war. Then he became Police Chief and is now personally answerable only to the Kremlin.'

'That I knew. But what about him?'

'First let me explain,' said Hans. 'Erich Mielke controls thousands of agents but his chief weapon is blackmail. Dossiers exist which cover the private lives of every leading industrialist, politician, intellectual and professional man in the Federal Republic. They have been compiled through phone tapping and opening correspondence, through agents working as servants in private houses or as employees within the offices of big businesses. Nurses, shopkeepers, even doctors and policemen have been used. Some of them worked voluntarily, others were forced to help because of personal indiscretions which Erich discovered and used for blackmail. Armed with all this he hoped to confuse and terrify West Berlin into submission, playing off one man against the other and the vanities of politicians against their fears. It was a more audacious system of informing than anything ever devised by Hitler, and for a while it looked like paying off. West Berlin became demoralized and Khruschev has been waiting the day when he might turn on the heat, insist upon the unity of Berlin and act knowing that our key leaders wouldn't lift a hand to stop him.'

'So?'

'So,' continued Hans, 'all went well enough until I began to work with the West Berlin Senate. We co-operated with the West Berlin Police Presidency in order to find an answer to Erich's activities and now we have completed our own dossiers. These are being published as a Black Book which will be sufficient answer to all those people who still don't understand the extent to which East German agents spy upon their own people, blackmail them into submission and bludgeon them into the ranks of a Com-

68

munist fifth column. And that in itself is good because it will give their victims the courage to resist. Moreover if guilty secrets were to be used against them everyone would now be prepared to believe that it was a frame-up. Our Black Book will therefore enable a man charged by his wife with infidelity, for example, to plead that the hotel bill was forged, the witnesses suborned and the whole thing a swindle to frighten him into serving the cause of Marx-Lenin-Stalin-Khruschev. Moreover, the Federal Courts will not now admit as evidence any material which springs from such a source, so everyone is quite well protected.'

'But why the excitement?' I asked. 'Get down to the things which matter.'

'If you were a German,' said Hans softly, 'these things would matter very much. But the big story is my reward for hard work. I had to study thousands of dossiers, examine tens of thousands of news items and speak with hundreds of people in order to cover this Black Book assignment, but in the course of it I met the one person who matters.'

'Who?'

'A Jew who became too intimate with one of Hitler's girl-friends. He escaped along with Erich Mielke and together they reached Russia.'

'Where is he now?'

Hans smiled with intense satisfaction and his voice became more gentle than ever. 'He is waiting for us near the airport and we are *en route* for South America. It is the done thing these days to go to South America.'

But I was becoming impatient. 'For goodness sake get on with it. Tell me the rest.'

'This man worked with Erich and reached a position of some authority. Indeed the Federal Government could be excused for trying him and executing him without delay. His record is deplorable. But he talked and talked plenty, therefore he is being spared.'

'How did you find him?'

'Once he was a handsome young Jew who was very attractive to women. Now he is a hard-as-nails middle-aged thug. But he is still a Jew and it seems that the call of the blood, ancestral ties and all the rest of it made him revolt.'

'Revolt against what?'

'The destruction of his people.'

'So he escaped and returned to Berlin?'

'Yes,' said Hans. 'He returned to Berlin and we found him posing as a Kazakhstan Jewish refugee.'

'How did he come into your orbit?'

'His current mistress was a suspect Communist informer . . . which makes an amusing coincidence. She was employed as a housemaid in an hotel used by political delegations and we were worried by leakages. Everyone in the hotel automatically became suspect and she was given a routine investigation.'

So far as Hans is concerned routine investigations include boy-friends, parents, the shops with which a man deals and even the number of cavities he has in his teeth. 'But how did you know it was the Jew who escaped with Mielke?'

'We naturally made a point of getting his finger-prints. One of our men served him with beer. The glass gave us a perfect set.'

'And do you mean to sit there and claim that you also had copies of those of the young Jew of twenty-five years ago?'

'We had. Hitler's people were thorough, and when the girl was being foolish they collected a set of her boy-friend's prints. They were photographed and filed in two places, one set in her own record and the other at Police Headquarters.'

'They survived the war?'

'Ach, yes. They were stored in deep vaults and are still in good condition.'

'They match?'

He quietly lit his pipe and smiled. 'They match.'

'So what do you want me to do?'

'Have a talk with him. He will interest you.'

'Where?'

Hans heaved himself on to his broad, flat feet and carefully adjusted his newly grown moustache, an old-Bill affair which did not improve him but which was part of his adjusted personality and background. 'The Jew now calls himself Spaak. He will be waiting for us in the Barnton Hotel. Come.'

70

8

The testimony of Spaak

THE Barnton Hotel is on the outskirts of Edinburgh and convenient for Turnhouse airport. Three men were waiting for us in the lounge. Two were nondescript young men of the type which I had come to associate with some of Hans's adventures. The third was a man in his late forties, clean-shaven and bony with deeply brown eyes and a thin scar curving across the right side of his forehead. Once he might have been handsome. Now he was almost distinguished.

Hans's voice assumed that timbre which it takes on only when he is doing something particularly distasteful and he did not introduce us. 'You will speak to this gentleman and answer his questions.'

'What made you leave Germany?'

'I was warned that the Nazis were on to me. They had found out about my association with the Führer's girl-friend. So I went into hiding in a friend's house. Later I joined Erich Mielke. We escaped to Belgium and from there went to Leningrad.'

'Why did you leave Russia?'

'I was sent to work with Erich in the Demokratische Republik.'

'Why did you then escape to the Federal Republic?'

'I suspected trouble.'

'What did you suspect?'

'The M.F.S.* has discovered that Russia is developing a new weapon. I believed that it might later be used to destroy Israel.'

'Why Israel?'

* The M.F.S. is the East German Ministry for State Security.

71

'Russia sees herself as future leader of the world. But first she wishes to eliminate the Western capitalist countries. When that has been done she will still have to face the peoples of Africa and Asia. To achieve stability she must give each of them something which they wish. Arab loyalty will be bought by destroying Israel. Some immense demonstration will then be made in Africa. This will end with whites being thrown out and black governments which are loyal to Russia being created everywhere. She will then try to come to terms with China and if her efforts fail she will rub out China with her new weapons.'

'What sort of weapons?'

The man shrugged his shoulders. 'I cannot be certain. We suspect that there are several different kinds: chemical substances which can be released as clouds of gas or as very fine sprays and which paralyse the faculties for several days . . . long enough for invading forces to establish and secure a bloodless victory. Then there are bacteriological bombs which may be too dangerous to use, viruses causing new illnesses and the like. There are also small cobalt bombs which could turn any given area of territory into a radio-active furnace in which no life would be possible for over twenty years.'

'Anything else?' I persisted.

'We had rumours of a weapon which manufactures a new-type energy. This energy is said to be capable of destroying not only life but matter itself.'

'Which did you think would be used?'

Again he shrugged his shoulders expressively. 'I thought "nerve gas" against the Western capitalist countries in the first instance, possibly also in parts of Africa and certainly against Israel.'

'How would it be delivered?'

'Either from long-range ballistic missiles or else from an artificial satellite cruising near the target area.'

'Manned or otherwise?'

'Otherwise. It will be some time yet before a man could accurately control such a weapon. At present it is easier to control it from the ground.'

'But you believe that war is probable?'

'It is certain.'

'How long is it since you escaped from East Germany?'

'I was in West Berlin for over three weeks before the police found me.'

'And yet during that time you did not report your discovery to any responsible person?'

He smiled faintly. 'Remember that I knew nothing of what life would be like in West Germany. I did not know whom I could trust. I had no wish to be put into jail and released later in the year by the Russians.'

'Who would have regarded you as a traitor,' I added.

'That is so,' he agreed.

'Then what did you hope to gain by escaping?'

'I intended to contact the Israeli Legation and ask for political asylum.'

'How did you escape in the first place?'

'The same way as most other people. By the underground railway.'

'And you were able to live for three weeks without being discovered or asked for papers?'

'My girl-friend had given me a room in her house.'

'Was she one of your own M.F.S. agents?'

He hesitated, and then: 'I cannot deny that she occasionally gave us information but she was not one of our regulars.'

'But you knew that she would help you even although you had never met?'

'Yes. She was sympathetic. She also liked money.'

'Where is she now?'

Hans spoke for the first time. 'She is now in prison. She will remain there for a long time.'

'But why your long delay in contacting Israel?' I persisted.

'I was afraid that they might have something against me.'

'Such as?'

'I had helped to clear Jews from Kazakhstan. It was an order and could not be disobeyed.'

'So you lived long enough in that Soviet State to learn the language and even pass yourself off as a Kazakhstani?'

'Yes.'

'And you killed some of your own people?'

'I supervised the work of others. I myself also did what others ordered.'

'If the German Federal Police had not discovered you what would you have done?'

'I might have contacted the Americans and told them everything.'

'Without fear?'

This unexpectedly needled him, for he looked at me angrily and his voice became harsh. 'You don't know what it means to have been a political refugee from your own country for years, to have lived under men to whom terror is an everyday business weapon like a fountain-pen or an adding machine. My life depended on doing what I was told. Mielke is ruthless. He had helped me and if I had disobeyed him in anything he would have had me shot. He wasn't a friend. As he became more and more powerful death meant nothing to him. He was worse than the Devil. I was terrified even to look him in the eyes in case he guessed that I hated him and was planning to escape. When I did get away I needed company and security. I needed love and the feeling that I was wanted.'

'So you bought both,' interrupted Hans.

'I did not,' he spat out venomously. 'The girl helped me because she liked me and was sorry for me. I paid her because she was poor and needed money.'

'Be that as it may,' said Hans, 'you kept this important information to yourself. You told no one and we have only your word for it that you would ever have told anyone. I still believe that you were only looking for a chance to get out of the country into a place where no one wanted you for murder.'

'And can you blame me if it were true? I have no reason to like Germany. Now I still wonder why I bothered to think about warning even Israel.'

'But why are you going to South America?' I asked.

'Ach, Herr Doktor,' said Hans smiling. 'I wondered when you would ask that. He hopes to make his peace with Israel if he can find Martin Bormann. It seems that the M.F.S. have clues as to where he may be. If Spaak finds him all will be forgiven.'

'So you all go to the Argentine?'

'Let us say,' replied Hans, 'that we all go to South America. South America is a big place and I too have clues about Bormann. Later we shall see if my clues and the other clues correspond. Until then we have an open mind about South America.'

'And why do you come to Edinburgh?'

'First,' said Hans, 'have you finished with this man?'

'One more question. When will the next war start?'

Spaak lit still one more cigarette. His fingers were trembling and his eyes hard. 'I have heard the date September 17th given,' he said. 'But I cannot be sure.'

At a nod from Hans the three men rose and left the room. The lounge was empty apart from a young couple chatting in the farther corner. 'And now,' said Hans softly, 'tell me about Sofia in detail. In absolute detail. Do not miss one single fact.'

He listened in silence, puffing stolidly at his usual clay pipe. When I was finished he looked at me long and thoughtfully. 'Some people are born lucky. You must be one of them, but I think you were spared for two reasons: first they did not wish to spoil the New Look approach which is at present lulling even the Americans into believing that the Bear is just a playful cub. Secondly they did rely on their hypnosis. But you have a strong will and were resistant. Even so you were lucky.'

'And Hanna?' I asked.

'I do not think we shall see her again.'

'And have you any other news?'

'No real news. But I do have ideas. They are not proof, only straws in the wind, but they add up to something important being in the air.'

'War?' I asked.

He nodded. 'Perhaps. But here are the things which matter as I see them.'

'First, Russia. Stalin wanted obedient tools which were sharpened on the edge of Marxism. But he did not want any intelligentsia or even any active Marxists. He simply wanted passive human instruments who would do as he wished. To achieve this he imposed a reign of terror and ruled by fear. He gained what he wanted, but towards the end of his life he suggested that his successors should pretend to swing in the opposite

75

direction. Indeed he made a point of ordering that these successors must assume friendship for the West in order to take the Free World off guard at a suitable moment.

'When Khruschev officially de-Stalinized the Soviet Union and heaped anathema on Stalin himself he was simply taking an obvious first step towards conditioning the West into believing that Russia had become approachable.

'Khruschev proceeded to liberalize the country, but he also pumped some partially forgotten Lenin dogmas into his current propaganda and in the end this return to Lenin convinced even himself of the essential rightness of Marxian teaching. World domination could only come through violence.

'But a younger generation has arisen who knew Marx and Lenin, the Revolution and Patriotic War only at second or third hand. Many were being trained as scientists and Khruschev has found this national mania for science to be a double-edged weapon, because he has discovered that youth cannot be taught any factual subject such as science with one part of its brain and the other part of its brain still remain capable of uncritically accepting falsehoods. In other words Russian youth has become less gullible than Khruschev expected.

'Moreover, educated Russian youth is not in sympathy with Lenin's ideals. World revolution and world war has no appeal. It just wants to put its own house in order, establish social justice and create a tolerable political system.

'He is now afraid that Russian youth, lacking Stalin's discipline, may not support any trumped-up story about capitalist aggression as an adequate excuse for war.

'Therefore if he is to get his way war must come soon. Moreover, it must start far outside Russia and be managed in such a fashion that Russia seems to be drawn into it for motives which will satisfy this young intelligentsia which has begun to think.

'Therefore,' continued Hans slowly, 'trouble will come where one least expects it.'

His arguments made sense. But where would be the trigger spot, I wondered.

'First,' said Hans, 'let us examine evidence to suggest that the great powers also realize the situation.'

76

'Khruschev decided to visit America and judge at first hand what sort of resistance might be expected from the American people. He is a superb showman and his American tour went better than anyone dared to expect in selling himself as a sort of father figure. Almost did he convince the States that he felt, thought and behaved like any typical American Big Businessman. Mr. K., they said, was something Americans could understand.

'And at the same time President Eisenhower's own tours were convincing Russians and everyone else that here was a man *they* could understand, that Americans were not so different really and that any differences which might exist could be ironed out.

'It had been felt by many people that John Foster Dulles was the evil man behind the scenes of American policy. When he died many Governments therefore believed that the way had been opened for a Soviet–American agreement of sorts.

'But this did not suit Khruschev's book at all. His goodwill tour had begun to kick back. Moreover, he himself had returned doubtful about even his own ability to capture America from within. In fact he now believes that only war can establish Soviet control in any at present free or uncommitted country.

'So 1959 ended with America enjoying high prestige amongst most smaller nations and with even young Russia realizing that the American peoples were not so very different from themselves.

'But the year also ended with Russia at loggerheads with a militant China determined to expand into the Asian sub-continent. China's behaviour shook everyone and Russia was forced to realize that here was a force to be reckoned with, that her yellow ally would no longer do as she was told by the Kremlin. America was also forced by events to accept that there was more to China than Formosa and that a Socialist China did exist as a major political factor in world politics. And even poor Nehru of India discovered that Asia was not, after all, united, that China would stab him in the back with as much pleasure as Russia or anyone else.

'The year ended with all the real cards in China's hands.'

'What about France?' I asked.

Hans smiled thoughtfully. 'General de Gaulle is the greatest living statesman in office. He is concentrating on minding his own business and in developing his own "secret" weapons.'

'Anti-matter?'

'Perhaps,' said Hans. 'But something good enough to keep even Russia at bay.'

'So the armament race is now in full swing,' I said.

'In full swing. But the advantage if anything is slipping away from Russia and indeed Khruschev's visit to China in September '59 was for one purpose only. To try and reassert his authority and teach China that for the next few years Communist policy will continue to be directed from Moscow and that force will be used only when the Kremlin says so.'

'And this,' I suggested, 'is the first tentative common purpose shared by both Moscow and Washington? Both are convinced of the need to contain Mao's China.'

'That is the position as I see it,' said Hans. 'The future, therefore, becomes more complicated than ever. But my guess is that Spaak's information is accurate. There will be sporadic trouble all over the world before many months have passed and Africa will soon become the epicentre of a political cyclone.'

'And Britain?' I queried.

Hans was tactful. 'Friends should not spy upon friends, but my information suggests that your Government is preparing deep shelters and protection for key personnel when war does come and America decides to "expend" your country.'

'What do you mean?'

'Underground fortress shelters were built at fabulous cost after the last war. They still exist and stretch below Holborn, Victoria, Whitehall, Leicester Square and other parts of London. But although they were made strong enough to withstand atomic blasts greater than anything visualized in 1946 your experts now say that they are out of date.'

'So?'

'So new shelters are being built elsewhere. These have everything. They are fitted with their own generating stations, air-conditioning systems, fuel and other reservoirs, supplies of food, refrigeration plants and photostat copies of every national record and fact which matters.'

78

'Who would use them?' I asked.

'The Cabinet, top Civil Servants, defence chiefs and perhaps also certain friendly embassy staffs. There will be radio links with the outside world and a complex system of underground cables will connect these shelters with other deep fortress pits housing various missiles. These missiles could therefore be fired from the central shelters many miles away or by any surviving personnel in their own area.'

'What about the British people?' I asked.

'Under the circumstances which we visualize,' said Hans, 'the British people will have to take what's coming to them. These will not be days when the Queen sets an example and strolls the bomb sites to give courage to others. Your Government is run by realists. As realists they know that Britain may have—to use the American expression—to be expended. Your anti-N.A.T.O., anti-American politicians also understand that and feel that Britain can be saved only through leaving N.A.T.O., by turning America out of Europe and then pledging neutrality.'

'Do you think they are wrong?'

'You *know* they are wrong. The first thing Russia does to people like them is to kill the worst and send the others off for re-education. The remainder of the population is then properly socialized. Later it is Communized.'

'And nothing can stop this?'

'There is one immediate hope. America's Polaris missile when fully developed will be perpetually at sea inside *Nautilus*-type submarines, each of which will carry hydrogen bombs with a destructive capacity greater than the total load of explosives used by all parties during the whole of the Second World War. Russia must therefore make any bid for world power before these submarines are in routine use, because afterwards she will be unable to destroy them all and must then accept that the price of any act of aggression on her part will be as many loads of hydrogen bombs as there are American atomic submarines still at sea.'

'Stalemate.'

'That is so. But at present there is no stalemate and Russia must fight this year or not at all.'

For a while we developed all his points but in the end he turned

79

again to the reason for his journey north. Spaak was being taken to South America more or less under guard although no one expected him to show the slightest resistance or even to attempt escape. Martin Bormann, the Nazi leader who had had so much to do with Hitler's rise to power, was now believed to be living in the Argentine. Efforts would be made to capture him. They were travelling as private citizens in a K.L.M. aircraft from London to Buenos Aires and had travelled via London in order to discuss the international implications of Hans's recent activities with Interpol. Hans had decided to make the trip north in order to talk over my adventures in Sofia, and as a gesture of goodwill to let me interview Spaak, whose hint of anti-matter would, he knew, interest me.

Hans was a philosopher. He had loved Hanna in a quiet, respectful fashion, admired her as a brave woman and found her easy to work with. But there had been no *grande passion*. He accepted her loss as a soldier accepts the loss of a comrade in arms. It was just the luck of the game. And in his more optimistic moods he still thought that she might 'turn up' when he least expected her. She had, he explained, a great instinct for survival.

Later we joined the others for a walk along Cramond Burn and upstream to the house where David Balfour* had lived with his uncle. Hans was a student of Scottish literature, and after Burns he admired Stevenson more than any other writer. Spaak was silent and the two younger men unobtrusive. All in all it was a macabre procession in such a gentle place and I was glad to see them off in a taxi to the city, where they passed the night in an hotel.

A few days later my thoughts were given a further unexpected twist by a brief message which read:

'Little Jack Horner. Humpty Dumpty.'

Our Turkish students were still active. They had exposed evidence enough to suggest that the Democrats were dealing with Russia and that preparations would be made to overthrow the régime.

*   *   *

* In Robert Louis Stevenson's *Kidnapped*.

That night Trudie listened to my latest news, and as usual her comments were to the point.

'We had better start packing for a return trip to Turkey. And this time we don't go through Sofia. The thought of that Stoicheva woman still makes me want to commit murder.'

In the end we did not pack for several more weeks and throughout them we watched the development of an incident which eventually proved to be the most important of all—the crash of Francis Powers's U.2 on 1 May 1960.

9

The last spy

'FRANCIS POWERS is the last spy before World War III,' said my brother Alistair.

An American U.2 had been shot down near Sverdlovsk on 1 May 1960 and one of the Free World's top secrets had become public property. Developed by the Lockheed Aircraft Corporation, the aircraft was the brain-child of Clarence Johnson, the head of Advanced Development Projects, and had been built for one primary purpose, espionage over the Soviet Union.

To do this a gigantic jet-glider was the only answer: a craft which would remain airborne even in the rarified atmosphere of 80,000 feet and yet maintain a cruising speed of something over 600 m.p.h. The machine had been built and tested within eighteen months. By late 1955 it was in operation. Officially it was used for sampling radio-activity and for weather reconnaissance. In fact U.2s served to put the greater part of the U.S.S.R. under a photographic and electronic microscope and hundreds of trans-Soviet flights were successfully accomplished throughout a five-year period. It was 1958 before Soviet intelligence admitted knowledge of them but even then the best Soviet defence was unable to cope.

MIG fighters had made desperate efforts to claw the U.2s down but even their cannon fell short in the thin air through which the jet-gliders continued to soar imperturbably on, recording, recording and still recording through powerful tele-lenses and other precision instruments every Soviet installation of importance. Even underground bases were marked through the use of infrared detection devices and for five years America's U.2s were the eyes and ears of the Free World.

'Unfortunately, however,' said Alistair, 'events now march so swiftly that almost any weapon is out of date even before it has left the blue-print stage and the U.2s had a longer innings than most.'

He had recently returned from a lengthy tour of Europe and was well placed to give a useful assessment of recent events. But my brother is cautious. He jumps to no conclusions and is impressed by nothing which cannot be verified. Not even when reported by myself.

The capture of Francis Powers and what might remain of his U.2 by the Russians had disturbed him more than any of my own adventures and he remained cynical about the reality of anti-matter as a practical offensive weapon.

But he was fascinated by the tactical stalemate which then existed. 'Think of it,' he said. 'American SAC squadrons have been based in Spain since 1958 when they were said to have created the final link in a so-called "deterrent circle" round Russia, other links extending as far as Africa, Greenland and Okinawa.

'But similar striking forces are also in perpetual readiness for action around the entire Communist periphery from the Karelian Isthmus to the edge of Alaska and from the Aral Sea to the frontiers of Turkey and Persia. Both sides own hydrogen bombs and cobalt bombs and neither can use them without reprisals. But,' he continued, 'these things are bows and arrows by comparison with developments which lie ahead. America will soon have her Polaris weapon and be capable of delivering hydrogen bombs from anywhere under the oceans of the world. But not for some months.' (In May 1960 they had none on the active list.)

'Russia has at least 450 orthodox submarines and a minimum of six nuclear-powered submarines also capable of delivering missiles of one sort or another from unexpected places. So Russia has a clear advantage at this point and must use it soon if it is going to be of any use to her. And remember,' he added, 'that Polaris weapons will not be a real deterrent until they are in full production with several hundreds constantly at sea to guard the Free World. And able to strike at any target, in any country, at any time.'

'So what will happen?' I asked.

'The present answer is not a stationary artificial moon a hundred miles above the Free World. It is a fast-moving sputnik loaded with nerve gases which can drench us from Hawaii to the Rhine or beyond within a few minutes. And a second or third on different orbits similarly drenching Australasia and Japan.

'Discharge of material from such a weapon could be controlled from the ground and Russia could ensure the unconsciousness of ninety-nine per cent of the Free World within ten minutes at any time of the day or night if she wished. Even allowing for imponderables of changing winds and the like. Also, her own key people could be protected against unexpected "drift" at different altitudes, because effective masks have now been developed with that very end in view.'

'Why does she not do this?'

'There is only one strong argument against. Even if your anti-matter stuff was practicable this is less dangerous and occupation troops would move in during the forty-eight-hour period of unconsciousness. When the Free World woke up its leaders would be dead and the remainder of the sheep prepared for fleecing and re-education.'

'What about the Polaris weapons? There would be time to deliver a heavy reprisal against Russia.'

'One nuclear-powered submarine,' said my brother, 'will carry sixteen hydrogen bombs representing a weight of explosives greater than the total tonnage of bombs used by all the sides during the Second World War. But since none will be in active service until the autumn Russia must move soon.'

'And what is the "argument against" to which you referred?' I asked.

'China. A ravaged Russia cannot take on a fit and undamaged Chinese People's Republic with any hope of survival.'

'How much would she be damaged?'

'Beyond anything she suffered last time. Probably various leaders would be killed. The machinery of government would have become impossible and she could control her conquests with nerve gases only if she operated from outside her own country.'

He hesitated and then slowly suggested a plan of campaign which some thought feasible.

Kremlin-provoked diversions would be created throughout the world and thereafter manipulated so as to give Khruschev opportunity to interfere whilst still posing as a liberal humanitarian and using methods which would be acceptable to a rising Russian intelligentsia which is now biased against war.

Having thus gained control of selected remote areas he would then fill them with technicians, troops (destined for use elsewhere), aircraft, missiles of all sorts and the complete impedimenta of modern technology. Turkey, Abyssinia, the Congo and parts of Indonesia or the Far East were a natural choice as bases. It was also worth remembering that a vast enclave of Abyssinia* had already been in Russian hands for several years and that that area alone could hold several millions of people. Several hundreds of thousands were already there and more were being added daily.

Having stocked such countries as he desired Khruschev could then use his nerve gases against his targets by delivery from fast, low-orbiting satellites. The Free World would, of course, retaliate but when her available missiles had been used up by surviving personnel the war would be over. Much of Russia would then have been devastated, but it was long odds against any missiles having been delivered against targets outside the Soviet Empire at this stage (May 1960). The Communist way of life would therefore continue from outside such bases as described and from them rehabilitation teams would be flown back to Mother Russia in order to salvage whatever might be possible.

The outlying bases would thus have served their purpose and would have been overcrowded for only a short period. Moreover the U.S.S.R. had sufficient heavy aircraft and petrol to ferry the huge numbers involved. Six trips by one would represent 1,000 people and since she had hundreds of machines capable of carrying such loads it was safe to estimate that she could ferry at least 75,000 persons daily, together with supplies of concentrated food.

Supplies of men and materials thus built up would be used first to occupy the unconscious Free World and then to do first-aid work in Russia. But whilst these ferry trips were continuing and the global operation was in progress Soviet missile sites would still continue to exist unharmed and poised for action in these outlying African or Middle Eastern bases. China would thus be

* At least twenty miles square, or 400 square miles, and capable of holding 8,000,000 people for at least a few days.

unable to offer opposition. The stricken Russia would therefore convalesce at leisure and later deal with China according to how the situation might develop but knowing that at no time could China have attempted war. December 1960 could see the world ruled from Moscow.

It was an ingenious suggestion, but complicated, and to my own mind anti-matter offered an easier solution. I also believed that further clues about it would soon emerge from Turkey.

Another message had arrived. 'All the King's horses and all the King's men couldn't put Humpty together again.'

Clearly preparations were now advanced and on 26 May a further signal reached us. 'Ride a cock horse to Banbury Cross.'

But it was still not possible for us to leave immediately for the Middle East, and on the following day, my birthday, 27 May, news of Turkey's Gentle Revolt hit the world headlines.

Events leading up to it had moved with irresistible logic and during May 1960 the milestones to disaster had been clearly obvious.

First, the Premier had suspended Ismet Inonü, leader of the Opposition, from the National Assembly and some days later law students had walked out of class at Istanbul University saying that now there was no law or Constitution in Turkey. Demonstrations which followed had ended with the deaths of several students killed by National Police on orders from their superiors. And in Ankara the military cadets had marched to Atatürk's statue to lay a wreath at its base, but in reality to dedicate themselves to his traditions and to the Revolution which they were already planning.

The Democrat Government had neglected even these clear warnings however, and on 27 May Ankara wakened to the sound of gun shots. Clattering tanks rumbled up Cankaya Hill to the Presidential Palace and within three hours most of the leaders were under arrest.

President Bayar had made an attempt to commit suicide—perhaps half-hearted. His daughter had stabbed one of the arresting officers.

Foreign Minister Zorlu had given himself up voluntarily, but Premier Adnan Menderes, together with Altemur Kilic, Director of Press, Radio and Tourism, were arrested by two aircraft as they raced by car towards Aydin, Menderes's home-town, from where they had hoped to reach the coast and escape to some Greek island. A Sabre jet had sighted the convoy and artillery spotter planes shortly afterwards landed fore and aft of the speeding cars. An hour later the Premier was under close confinement in the War Ministry.

Within a few days the most hated man of all, Namik Gedik, had committed suicide by jumping from a window in Ankara's military college.

On 28 May it was clear that the revolt enjoyed popular support. General Cemal Gursel was in effective control, working with a Committee of National Unity comprising the cream of the Army's most able younger officers, and already the General had pledged Army honour to remain in N.A.T.O., to fulfil all the country's treaty obligations and re-establish parliamentary government forms at the earliest opportunity. Imprisoned journalists were released on the same day and 'Freedom' became the revolutionary slogan.

Trudie and I wished that we had been there. In the immediate aftermath of the swift revolt there would be plenty of work to do investigating suspects, scrutinizing Democrat records which hitherto had been inaccessible and rounding up minor officials suspected of corruption.

In the midst of all that, I felt, surely some evidence must come to light which would confirm or deny our suspicions about world trends.

*   *   *

All of June passed before we could rejoin Turan, Yildiz and the others but when we did meet they were bursting with news.

'We know why the Russians were so cross about Francis Powers and his U.2,' smiled Yildiz. 'It is wonderful to live now in a free country but it is almost as wonderful to know why the Soviet Union is so angry with America.'

'Soon there will be war,' said Turan. 'Unless our leaders and the world's leaders are very clever.'

'Or unless God decides to interfere,' said Cemil. 'And if ever the Great God needed to interfere it is now.'

Our meeting had been arranged in the Park Hotel. This is rather

87

a ramshackle building with bedrooms overlooking the Bosphorus and they had chosen it because during Menderes's years in power he had always used it in preference to the Hilton as his Istanbul headquarters. It now amused them to sit in a place so closely associated with the enemy.

We were speaking on the balcony outside our bedroom, and as the students again explained, 'It is wonderful to be able to say what one likes without fear of microphones or National Police.'

'And National Police are the key words,' said Turan. 'Our story is almost unbelievable, but you must let us tell it in our own way.

'When you left us almost a year ago we didn't agree that any Turk could be a traitor and we were not really suspicious about these Soviet ships. We were more anxious about staying out of prison ourselves and it was Yildiz who really convinced us that Soviet tourists were a cover-up for other things.'

'Because I was lucky,' Yildiz continued. 'I had noticed some tourists from Roumania outside Aya Sophya and I knew one of them by sight because when my uncle was at the Embassy in Bucharest pictures of certain V.I.P.s had been taken at a May Day party. This man was one of them and my uncle knew him to be a leading Roumanian terrorist. He was exactly like his photograph and I did not believe that such a person would come on a holiday cruise to Stamboul. So I followed him.'

As I have remarked before, Yildiz has a fine instinct which rarely lets her down. The Roumanian had drifted away from the company and had visited a police station not far from the Konya Restaurant. He had been received by Namik Gedik's Secretary and the Minister of the Interior himself had arrived by car a few moments later. The Roumanian had returned to the ship only seconds before the gangway was lifted.

'So,' continued Yildiz, 'I wanted to discover what these men had in common.'

'And did you?' asked Trudie.

'Not at first,' said Turan, 'but when we heard Yildiz's evidence we became more interested.'

Our friends then unravelled a long story of shadowing, eavesdropping and even the discreet buying of information, but their story added up in the end to their earlier belief that Namik Gedik had been in contact with Communists of various nationalities, that he had made phone calls to the Russian Embassy, that he had often been seen dining with a lovely Bulgarian woman and that he had tightened up security measures to such a pitch that no spoken or written opposition was possible. They also came to believe that certain Democrat leaders themselves lived in fear of his department and that he might even have been planning a coup in order to establish himself as a modern-style dictator.

But oddly enough they had not said much about their impressions to any of their Republican or Army friends because they realized that revolution or civil war had then become inevitable and that the Democrats would be overthrown for entirely different reasons. They felt that Namik Gedik would be punished for his many other crimes at a later date and that anything they might then say would not influence matters very much.

'So,' continued Turan, 'we threw in our lot with those who were preparing the revolt and the only really active thing I did was to be with the party which went to Gedik's house on 27 May to make the arrest.'

It must have been a dramatic moment when several students, army cadets and officers approached his house in Ankara's Bahcelievler district and the Minister of the Interior opened the door. When he saw the students he laughed and ordered them away saying: 'Get out. I have more guns in this house than you have in your whole organization.'

But after a short scuffle he was arrested and taken to a waiting car. Neighbours had gathered in the darkness to watch and as the most hated man in Turkey was rushed down his garden-path several spat in his face.

'It was then that he may have realized for the first time how much he was despised,' continued Turan, 'because no one had any sympathy for him. Indeed people were already demanding his death.'

When the car drove off crowds continued to hang about in the streets. Other Ministers lived in the same area—a fashionable suburb close to Atatürk's Mausoleum—but whilst the onlookers were content to stand and watch, Turan with his friends searched Gedik's house, ransacked his study and collected a host of letters, dossiers, state papers and private diaries which were later turned over to the Army. One envelope, however, contained photographs and several typewritten documents, some signed by the Soviet Ambassador. There were marginal notes in Gedik's own sprawling script and even a quick appraisal had been enough to show that the thing was red-hot evidence of high treason. Fortunately Turan had found this himself.

'Why did you not hand it over?' I asked.

'Because I knew that all arrested Ministers would later be tried in court for breaking the Constitution and for other offences. The trials would attract world attention and I did not like the idea of any Turk being publicly found guilty of conspiracy with the Soviet Union against his own people.'

'So what did you do?'

'He decided to keep it for a few days whilst we thought matters over,' said Yildiz. 'But when Gedik killed himself that solved our problem.'

'What problem?'

'The letters prove that our earlier guess was correct, that he had hoped to do a deal with Russia and take over here as Police dictator . . . a sort of Turkish Stalin.'

'So if the students and Army had not acted as they did the Democrats would still have been overthrown, but this time by their own top policemen.'

'Correct,' said Turan. 'And we would have had a full-blown police state with Menderes and Bayar as first victims and with Soviet occupation troops to back the Gedik puppet government.'

Gedik must have realized that death by hanging was inevitable. He had no way of knowing who had taken possession of all his papers or of guessing that a few students were guarding the ones which mattered most. He had been lodged in the top floor of Ankara's military college. The room was shared with Etem Menderes—the former Minister of Defence but no relation to the Prime Minister although of the same name. The two men had gone to bed, lights were burning in the room and the door was still slightly open awaiting a return visit by their guard. Menderes later reported that Gedik suddenly jumped out of bed and had some sort of hysterical fit. Then screaming 'Oh God' he had rushed to the small window and thrown himself through, breaking glass and frame alike.

'Was it suicide?' I asked.

'Yes. If we had wanted to kill Gedik or anyone else we could easily have done so when they were arrested. That is the traditional revolutionary approach but we wanted to create a new technique and we did not wish to soil our revolt with killing of any kind, anywhere or at any time.'

'But you still did not give the letter to the Committee of National Unity,' I said.

Our student friends were polite but firm. 'The Committee is busy and has enough to do without our complicating matters. Gedik is dead and the Russian letters implicate no one else in our country. The papers can be of no value at the trials.'

'But,' said Cemil, who had until now been content to listen, 'they are important for the outside world.'

'So what did you do?'

'I took photostat copies,' said Yildiz, 'and sent one of each to the American, British, French and West German Ambassadors.'

'Signed?'

'No. Only a covering note explaining that the enclosures had been found in Gedik's safe.'

But I was becoming impatient and had been kept guessing long enough. Where did Francis Powers figure in all this? Why were the pictures so important?

Turan slowly opened the envelope and handed over the photographs, together with a translation of documents. They made shocking reading and in particular the pictures partially solved the problem of anti-matter.

Gedik had in fact been preparing his own coup.

The Soviet Union was backing him to the hilt.

He had undertaken to break Turkey's N.A.T.O. and other alliances.

His first act after establishing himself as dictator would have been to sign a formal pledge of union with the U.S.S.R. and agreement to the establishment of unlimited Russian bases throughout Central Anatolia and as far west as Fetiye, with special reception camps for Soviet personnel around the air bases of Kars, Erzerum and Van.

These air bases would have been immediately expanded to accept large troop-carrying aircraft, and temporary camps would have been erected in their vicinity.

The new régime would have been protected by Soviet aircraft and soldiers.

All other foreigners would have been deported.

Turkey would thus have become the Soviet Union's second Middle-Eastern satellite.

Guarantee of Soviet strength was also provided by pictures which, said the covering documents, had been taken by the American pilot Francis Garry Powers whilst on an espionage mission over Soviet territory. They showed that the American spy had secured pictorial evidence of the effectiveness of the Soviet Union's latest weapon. On testing grounds, a range of mountains more than 5,000 feet high and ten miles long had been completely removed from the surface of the earth. Only a naked scar remained to show where this new energy had been applied. If it had been compared with earlier pictures taken by other U.2s the Western Powers would have gained evidence of Soviet advances in this field, but unfortunately Soviet interception had made this impossible. The spy Powers had been brought down and would later be tried before a Soviet court.

Copies of the picture were being delivered by hand. They would be returned by the same messenger and were intended for the Minister of the Interior's own exclusive use in order to convince him that his own best interests lay in a policy of total co-operation with the Soviet Union.

He was also reminded that the Soviet Union would not interfere in matters which were exclusively Turkey's own internal affairs but that in all other respects Gedik would be obliged to follow the official party line and obey instructions from Moscow.

Clearly the Army and students had arrived at the psychological moment and the messenger had been unable to take them back. Francis Powers's true achievement had been made available to the Free World only because of a monumental coincidence.

'Perhaps, after all,' said Cemil, 'God had decided to take a hand.'

10

Signposts to chaos

EVENING had fallen over the Bosphorus and already stabbing headlights were probing the velvet darkness above the Adriatic shore. A few ferry-boats bustled from Stamboul towards Princes Islands and the rocky islet where all the Democrat Party were now imprisoned.

Tiny twinkling windows marked Topkapi Palace above the trees beyond Seraglio Point, and the ship upon which we had done our Black Sea trip one year earlier was now lying in midstream off Galata Quaie. Much had happened in the interval. Hank, I reflected, had not, after all, been 'off-course'. The little hills really *had* disappeared. The Americans in distant Trabzon had had every reason to be scared. The 64,000-dollar question was quite simple. What would happen next?

Had any of the Embassies taken action in the light of Yildiz's photographs?

Did Washington, London, Bonn and Paris realize the implications of the tactical coup which was being hatched in Moscow's Kremlin?

'But do *you* know what is really hatching?' said Yildiz. 'We still have a few surprises.'

'Such as?'

She handed over more photostats of letters and a document which had been translated into English. 'I also sent these to the Embassies a few days later. They are copies of more papers found either in Gedik's safe or in vaults housing some of his department's archives, but dated a few weeks earlier.'

'How did you get hold of them?'

'Affairs were confused for several days after the revolt. Many people had to be rounded up. Universities and offices, banks and all government departments were closed and during that time we were going all out to collect evidence of Democratic corruption. The boys worked here and myself with Turan in Ankara. Every member of the Parliamentary Party had to be arrested and his affairs examined. We had access to many secrets and I took pictures of everything important. Some are extremely interesting.'

'Where are the originals?'

'Probably in the hands of the Committee of National Unity. Or else they may be with the investigating committee.'

'The Public Prosecutor, you mean?'

'And his department. But evidence is still arriving daily.'

'And it will be filed within the same building?'

'Not necessarily. But we have so many documents that it won't matter very much if a few are missing. There are still enough left to hang the guilty.'

The papers in my hand held enough evidence to have someone not only hanged, but hanged, drawn and quartered, and it was little wonder that Namik Gedik had accepted suicide as the easiest way out. Yildiz's other papers were virtually a blue-print for world war and revolution ante-dating the Powers pictures by some days but intended to underline the part which the Minister of the Interior was expected to have played had matters worked out differently. And as I read the summarized synopsis it became difficult to see how any satisfactory answer could be found.

The sequence of events was already unfolding.

The Soviet Union was backing civil war in the Congo, supporting Lumumba and so contriving developments that Belgian and other 'white' inhabitants were being forced to leave the country. 'In due course,' said the memorandum, 'Soviet scientists and other technicians will demonstrate to the African peoples that their future peaceful development can lie only within the sphere of co-existence and constructive co-operation with the Soviet Union. The peoples of Africa must then be persuaded that their progress and continued peaceful development can spring only from close

94

alliance with their brothers in the U.S.S.R. who have watched their efforts to achieve independence and self-expression throughout Africa.'

A note had been added in Gedik's handwriting. 'How will this demonstration be arranged? Against whom will it be directed? When is it due to take place?'

The document continued:

Soviet technicians, military and civilian personnel, cultural and other representatives will later be posted to the Congo, Abyssinia and Turkey as a first step towards replacing those outmoded Capitalist social forms which have for so long retarded progress in these areas. Preparations for their reception in our Abyssinian base are already advanced. But the Soviet Government believes that political stability will have been achieved throughout the Congo before mid-August 1960 and that the Congolese peoples will thereafter swiftly prepare similar bases for their Soviet allies. The Soviet Government therefore considers that Turkey must also be liberated from the yoke of Democrat war-mongering imperialists without delay in order that similar facilities may also be set up throughout those designated areas of Anatolia which have been judged most suitable. In order to assist you in this great task Soviet troops and aircraft will be at your disposal to control possible opposition from war-mongering elements still at large. The Soviet Government further suggests that you should engage upon this operation on or before 15 July 1960. By so doing you will be co-operating with your allies in other places and making it possible for the Soviet Government to engage systematically upon its task of removing the sores of American and Western European Imperialism from the Free Nations of the world. It is expected that you will have assumed office as President of Turkey not later than 16 July, by which date all leading national traitors should have been eliminated. It is further expected that priority will immediately be given for the reception of substantial numbers of Soviet economic and other experts, military and civil advisers and masses of skilled workers as a first step towards the reconstruction of your country along the paths of continuous peaceful co-existence and co-administration with the Soviet Union.

At this point further pencil notes had been added:
'What is meant by peaceful co-administration?'
'Define the word "continuous".'
'How many "personnel" are to be expected?'
The memorandum ended with one cryptic sentence:

The Soviet Union expects that you will organize your affairs according to this time-table knowing that the might of your Soviet ally lies strongly behind you and that you will wish to take your place amongst those great patriots privileged to lead the free peoples of the world in their task of liberating all mankind from the corruption of Western imperialism.

'And now read this,' said Turan quietly. 'We also collected it from Gedik's own house on the night he was arrested. At that time it made no sense but now we are not so sure.'

He handed over a fragment of paper which had been badly crumpled and was partially burned. The typescript was in French and a fair translation would be: '. . . towards Rhodes, in the Far Eastern Theatre and with the help of our brave ally Raul Cas . . .'

'Castro?' I queried.

'Fidel's brother,' said Yildiz.

For a while we were silent. There was too much about which to think and none of it seemed even vaguely to be possible in such a lovely place. The moon had risen high and was glowing over Leander's little islet, the white gables of its tiny castle glinting like silver. A row of coloured lights across the waters marked the most western Luna Park in Asia and on the veranda café below beautiful women and gravely dignified men were watching the play of ferry-boats and ships on the Bosphorus.

Carefully I tried to match the latest news with the course of world events during previous months.

Britain had officially announced cancellation of her Blue Streak Rocket project. Considering my own experience everything pointed to a leakage and I believe my talkative Paris acquaintance had said too much to the wrong people.

96

Mr. Macmillan had completed certain unprecedented tours in some of the Commonwealth's trouble-spots. He had gone out of his way to contact discontented leaders. In South Africa he had even criticized Nationalist policies in the full publicity of Parliament and before all shades of political opinion. He had predicted disaster if Apartheid continued to divide the colours and had gone further than any other British statesman towards interfering in the internal affairs of a friendly state. Only grave necessity could have driven him so far.

At home powerful elements were campaigning to have American bases closed not only in Britain but throughout Europe. Neutralism was in the air and tempers had already risen so high that the British Socialist Party looked like committing suicide rather than risk death from nuclear weapons. But more important still was the fact that Fred Hand* had stated his knowledge of things to come and his fear that Britain would be 'expended' by her allies in the event of war.

Support to this fear was given by the underground shelters at present being created by the British Government, shelters designed to survive even a nuclear war and to hold all documents which might help to continue the British way of life to a longer future.

The behaviour of Mr. Khruschev in Paris had shown that the carefully cultivated façade was a sham, that Russia's New Look was false and that the bluff Soviet leader could threaten death to humanity as easily as he could kiss babies or pat the heads of little children. He had been revealed as a man more dangerous than either Hitler or Stalin.

His influence was behind that mob rule which had driven the Japanese Prime Minister to cancel President Eisenhower's visit to Tokyo in June: the same influence was stirring up frictions in the West Indies and was supporting Castro in Cuba. His agents were fomenting strife throughout Africa, and in Abyssinia he was only awaiting the death of an Emperor before pouncing on the nation from his huge, diplomatically protected enclave near Addis.

The Berlin question also continued to simmer in spite of Hans's good work and it could be brought to the boil whenever Marshal

* See page 38.

97

Malinovsky or Mr. Khruschev decided that heat would suit their policies.

Iraq was settling into the rut of semi-Communist discipline and would do as she was told by Moscow.

Blood was being shed all over Africa under the influence of Communist-backed nationalism—a strange mixture, but apparently popular in some places—whilst in South Africa matters were rising to that crescendo of hate which might well provoke civil war and that despite Mr. Macmillan's earlier advice.

The American and Russian leaders had covered more territory than any statesmen in world history, each trying to sell his own wares in the teeth of strong opposition, and each trying to win or woo support for policies which could end only with the destruction of the other.

Proof of Soviet intentions to 'take over' Turkey and use a Gedik government as 'front' to its real intentions was absolute and the coup had been frustrated only because of prompt action by the country's far-seeing students and an army which could not be corrupted. General Gursel and his Committee of National Unity had saved not only Turkey, their actions had indirectly exposed conspiracies intended to destroy all that Christian and Moslem culture and civilization alike had achieved throughout 2,000 years of struggle.

France might, in the event, have been saved only through General de Gaulle, but even he was still faced by a Communist-inspired war in Algeria . . . again nationalism urged on by the sinister forces of underground Communist agents.

Italy was also teetering towards the Left and every other impoverished nation from Rio del Oro to distant Cambodia was similarly being undermined by Kremlin intrigue.

But throughout all this welter of fact there was a common denominator of purpose, a red rope of treachery intended to bind those remaining democracies and independent countries to the Men of Moscow and the doctrines of Marx–Lenin–Stalin. One other fact also stood starkly clear: Russia not only possessed a weapon of fantastic power but was prepared to use it in the near future.

It now also seemed probable that Alistair's impressions might well be accurate, and that the Kremlin was even prepared to write off much of the Soviet Union, together with many of her people, in order to overthrow capitalism, Christian civilization and every other nation cherishing liberal ideals or personal freedom from the Tonga Isles to Iceland.

But Alistair's belief that Khruschev was planning to rehabilitate his stricken country from prepared outside bases was not only original, it was the only possible answer to the stalemate which had been created. And it was also practicable from the Soviet angle because Khruschev knew as well as any man that neither America nor Britain would destroy innocent peoples or bombard the Congo, Turkey or any other similar place under present circumstances.

'Well,' said Yildiz. 'You seem very thoughtful?'

'Does your Government know all this?' I asked.

'I imagine so.'

'But you are not sure.'

'There has been no official announcement about anything affecting other countries excepting General Gursel's statement that Turkey would continue to honour all her treaty obligations.'

'Have any of you noted unusual comings or goings between the Western Ambassadors and the Committee of National Unity?'

'They have been in almost daily contact,' said Cemil. 'I am sure that most of the high-ups know about everything which matters.'

Another point occurred to me. Who had delivered the Powers pictures to Namik Gedik? Who was the mysterious beauty with whom he had been seen dining?

'You said that she was a Bulgar?'

'I think so,' said Turan. 'That is her nationality on the hotel register.'

'Name?'

'Paula Karsovina.'

'Young?'

'Early thirties perhaps.'

'Beautiful?'

'Striking. She was magnificent.'

'She was blatant, hard and cruel,' said Yildiz slowly. 'These boys never see a woman without thinking of bed. When I see a woman I try to look at her soul. This woman was bad.'

'You mean the one he dined with,' I said.

'Yes. We do not know who handed over the pictures on the night of 26 May.'

'What happened to the other people in the house that evening?'

'All were accounted for. There were no foreigners.'

'Surely the messenger, whoever it may have been, must have realized that to leave such things behind, under the circumstances, would lead to discovery of the very pictures which were so secret? That sooner or later the pix would reach people who mattered and that they would then get a slant on Russia's new weapon?'

'But things happened quickly,' said Turan. 'Not more than twenty seconds would elapse before we were in his study after ringing his door-bell.'

'Then the messenger must have moved even more swiftly.'

'We met no strangers. But the windows were open and some-one could easily have escaped through them.'

'Leaving the pix?'

'Gedik had put them in his safe, perhaps for security whilst he was out of the room. The door was locked.'

'How did you open it?'

'His keys were taken before he was driven away.'

'It all sounds very confused and badly arranged,' I said slowly. 'It doesn't really seem credible.'

The boys were offended. The revolt had been a dangerous adventure which had gone better than anyone could have expected. How could I expect people to guess what might be found in the house, or to expect that a Soviet agent might have been inside, that Turkey's Minister of the Interior was in possession of pictures taken by Francis Powers's U.2 or that the man had himself been preparing revolution of a different sort for his own purposes?

'Perhaps I can help,' said Yildiz. 'This Bulgarian woman who knew Gedik, the one with whom he dined, was also friendly with a Chinese who lives in Ankara and works for a business house with Far Eastern interests. His address was discovered in one of the diaries picked up at police headquarters in Istanbul. I noted it

100

down because we have few Chinese people in Turkey and I thought it was just possible that he might be the one I had seen with the Bulgarian woman some weeks earlier. He uses the name Sun Yutan and he might, perhaps, be able to tell us something.'

'How?'

'We could arrange to have him arrested.'

'But this person may be perfectly honest,' I protested.

'No honest man would dine with that woman,' said Yildiz. 'And his police record suggests he might be a spy so that is reason enough for getting hold of him.'

'If he were a spy he would have run away by now.'

'Which shows how little you know of spies,' said Yildiz, 'because if he has been a good spy he will believe that he can stay with safety.'

'If his background is so good how did the police get on to him?'

Cemil was amused. 'My friend, it is an old Turkish police custom to be suspicious of foreigners. Your own name was also in the diary. Trudie and yourself are listed as "People to watch. At present do not interfere".'

But I did not join in the laughter. I did not like the words 'at present'. And vaguely I sensed that behind all this we would eventually discover traces of Paula Stoicheva, the woman with no soul.

Surely no two persons could have the same Christian name and be beautiful to men, but blatant, hard and cruel in the eyes of another woman!

'I don't know whether she will prove to be the same woman or not,' said Trudie, 'but I do know that these documents are signposts to chaos. I am beginning to feel frightened.'

11

The capture and interrogation of Sun Yutan

I SENT an account of the whole story to Dag Hammarskjöld in early August 1960. The students did not allow me to keep copies of the pictures. Nor did they give me original documents, not even the scrap of paper naming Raul Castro. Indeed they were possessive about anything which might have led to Gedik's treachery becoming provably known to a wider audience and although their story is essential to world understanding of Soviet strategy they do not approve of my using it in this book.

Turks are above all loyal, and written evidence of Gedik's intention to give the U.S.S.R. bases in Anatolia was a slight upon their country about which they were sensitive. Nor could they remove from their minds the possibility that others had been implicated in the plot. As people of common sense, however, they had done what they could to inform the world of Soviet plans and had warned the four Embassies which chiefly mattered.

But it did not seem to be enough and I slept better having posted all that I knew to the United Nations Secretary-General. One copy was forwarded by air-mail from Ankara. A second was posted later in the month from Piraeus.

With the arrest of Sun Yutan a week later, however, my own angles upon world affairs were again swiftly re-orientated and for days on end life in Turkey acquired the colour of a thriller novel until I had to remind myself again and again that truth is stranger than any fiction which can be created.

It is an open secret that every country has a department whose activities it prefers to disown. Indeed during recent years even Britain and America have been forced to accept that phone tapping, hidden microphones and systematic informing are not the especial province of the Soviet Union. But they know less of more sinister matters, and the House of Commons had lately risen in wrath to defend the rights of the individual when an astonished Britain learned something of Professor Alexander Kennedys' researches in brain-washing suspects, extracting evidence of falsehood from political or other poseurs, and in general doing the dirty work which keeps a democracy clean.

Turkey was no democracy in mid-1960—not even after the revolt—but she was determined to become a liberal Western-style parliamentary democracy as soon as possible and was leaning backwards to avoid anything which could be regarded by the Great Powers as unconstitutional. In fact it was better for the Committee of National Unity not to let its left hand know some things at least which its strong right hand might be forced to do and the examination of Sun Yutan (and others of whom I knew nothing) was one of them.

He was removed from his house in the small hours of the morning with a blanket wrapped around his head. None of his captors spoke a single word and he had no means of knowing for sure who had seized him.

He was a lithe little man, but powerful and possessed of immense resources of character. He behaved with a cunning almost equal to that shown by his inquisitors, struggled not at all, said little and at first was prepared to lie doggo.

A closed commercial vehicle then rushed him to Ankara airport where he was heaved aboard a transport plane whose engine was already ticking over. Only at the door did he make his bid for escape. The guards had been reassured by his unexpected passivity and when they least expected it he blindly kicked one in the groin, grabbed another in a ju-jitsu grip which almost broke his wrist and in the same second attempted to dive down the low step-ladder. He succeeded only in uncovering his head before a crashing blow from a short baton knocked him unconscious.

He was swiftly bundled into the aircraft and recovered consciousness ten minutes later. A trickle of blood was coursing down his forehead and he looked a pitiable object. His captors all wore hoods of white cotton gathered together under the chin. Their hands were hidden by gloves which concealed every clue as to age and none of them spoke one word.

The object was to disorientate him completely and to make it impossible for him to assess where he might be taken. His temporary unconsciousness had made that relatively easy, but as there was no knowing how much of it had been absolutely genuine he was kept airborne for over three hours, long enough for him to have been landed in almost any Balkan or Middle Eastern country. In fact he touched down at the same airport from which he had taken off and was whisked away in the same closed van to the Altindag district of Ankara and to a specially prepared house.

His room was sound-proof with beaver boarding and packing of glass-wool lining brick walls which were also covered on the outside by a similar insulation of glass-wool and asbestos sheeting. Double doors were proof against outside light. The small toilet which had been prepared in one corner lacked chain or metal attachments and a mattress lay upon the floor. Ventilation was controlled by a portable extractor fan let into the high ceiling but in midsummer there was no need for a heating unit. Water was delivered in a plastic container holding approximately one litre. Food was also served in plastic bowls.

A panel of one-way glass had been sunk into the rather high ceiling and was so angled as to ensure a complete view of the whole floor. From below it was noticeable only as a mark upon the frieze which might well have been a badly repaired plaster job.

Only one other feature remains to be described. A small light strip had been placed almost flush with the ceiling but close to the one-way spy-glass. The light was subdued but adequate and could not be increased in intensity. Close by its base a tiny microphone could transmit to the room above when necessary. A small loudspeaker was incorporated beside it through which sound could be transmitted from the room above. Otherwise there was nothing of any kind in the room.

Only six people had access to the house: the quiet man who more than most protects Turkey's homeland and who may loosely be described as chief of underground counter-espionage. For obvious reasons his name must remain secret and I shall call him Ahmed. Turan and his friend Orhan Bey were privileged to assist as their reward for discoveries which had shattered even Ahmed's grave composure. Two other members of Ahmed's staff had responsibility for guarding the place and I myself was included as the well-disposed 'outsider' who had tried in various ways to help both the Turkish people and the new government. I therefore had the distinction of taking part in an inquisition which must rank as one of the most significant in world history.

But for one whole day Sun was left alone in his silent cell. The dim light burned during every hour and he had been stripped of every possession excepting his underpants and silken singlet. His teeth had been examined whilst he was in the plane and everyone was reasonably certain that he could not 'do a Goering or a Himmler' and break some mysterious capsule of prussic acid which had been overlooked.

He wore no rings and even the interior of his body had been explored—again whilst he was unconscious and in the plane—for any poison vial or hidden weapon which might by a far stretch of imagination have been carried within his bowel.

We each took one hour in four to study him through the window.

It was a monotonous vigil and for almost a day he was content to lie on his back . . . simply staring.

Food was delivered by a hooded guard at irregular intervals, the first around nine a.m., the second about ten-fifteen, the third at four and the last meal at midnight, because it was hoped that such irregularity would further serve to increase that sense of disorientation which we were trying to establish as a first step towards conditioning him for questioning.

During the whole of my first watch he lay motionless upon his mattress breathing quietly, with his eyes open and in a state of apparently complete physical relaxation. Indeed his ability to relax was enviable and at one stage Turan likened him to a dog dozing after a long walk.

But he was no dog. And he was not dozing. Rather was he preparing himself for whatever might follow and we visited him for the first time on the morning of the second day. There were three of us, all hooded and each speaking a different language, French, English and German, as part of the continued effort to disorientate.

'What is your name?' said Ahmed in German.

There was no reply.

'What is your name?' asked Turan in French.

'What is your name?' I continued in English.

There was still no reply.

For over one hour we asked the same repetitive question and for over one hour Sun lay upon his back staring at us impassively.

And then he spoke. 'Why do you want to know?'

He had opted for English and his accent was good, but no one paid attention to his reply, and instead the same monotonous round continued, but this time always in English from ourselves.

In the end Ahmed stepped forward, and speaking in a quiet, reasonable manner said: 'No one in this world knows where you are. You have disappeared from the surface of the earth. But your name is John Sung. You come from Shanghai and you have enemies who wish to kill you.'

For a few moments longer Turan and I continued the alternating chorus. 'You have disappeared from the face of the earth. No one knows where you are but your name is John Sung and you come from Shanghai.'

His only response was the slow breaking of a sweat bead upon his forehead and the slightest ever increase in a pulse rate which remained slow at sixty-three per minute. In the end we withdrew and for the remainder of our second day he was left alone apart from the serving of food four times in the space of six hours. He went to the toilet five times and washed himself carefully on two occasions in the tepid water of his plastic bottles. There was no towel and his only real flicker of reaction was a gesture of disgust when he discovered that he must either remain damp or else use his singlet.

But after his fourth meal of the day he lay down and slept. When he wakened it was really only late evening but he became restless when food did not arrive and we realized that he believed it to be morning and that our ruses were succeeding.

106

The second night passed badly and he began to pace the room. He looked both older and less dangerous under a two-day growth of scruffy beard.

I was still dissatisfied about the whole affair and it seemed hard that a man should be arrested because Gedik's police had been suspicious of him, or because he was a Chinese and had been seen speaking with Gedik's Bulgar friend. But Ahmed was only amused by my doubts.

'An honest man,' he said, 'would have answered our questions. An honest man would have spoken to his guards. An honest man would not have lain as he did hour after hour gathering his strength for some battle of wits with an enemy he could not know. Already I believe that Yildiz has got on to something important here. He will have much to say before we are finished.'

'Was she annoyed that you kept her out of things?' I asked.

He smiled faintly. 'Yildiz was annoyed. But this is not a job for women and it is better that she knows nothing about it.' He then looked at me rather coldly and added briefly, 'I sometimes also wish that you knew nothing about it.'

Orhan Bey arrived at the end of his watch with our first slight piece of news. 'The man is getting worried. He is biting his nails a little and he dislikes his beard.'

But I remembered the experiences of those who had been questioned by the Russians or others and was against breaking the tension by more questions. Everyone who has experienced this ordeal of repetitive questioning knows that the greatest of all arts is the decision when to speak. Sometimes the inquisitor may give up in despair at that very crucial moment when the subject is ready to break, and so lose what may be the only chance.

Others know that at a certain stage of anxiety when loneliness is pressing in upon all sides and when fear is taking hold of the senses that a return of even the inquisitors can break the spell and restore courage which was fading.

My friends were rather against this reasoning but they were persuaded to wait and we returned in the early morning.

'Well, John Sung from Shanghai,' said Ahmed quietly. 'Have you anything to say this evening?'

The man was sitting morosely upon his mattress and staring

at the cold linoleum floor. His voice was quiet. 'Who are you?'

And then the second stage of our approach began with a series of prepared questions asked slowly, one after the other, but returning haphazardly to earlier questions and thus repeating in irregular fashion a jumble of disconnected subjects over a wide field. And whilst we grilled him Turan watched reactions from above, noting his response to our broadly cast bait and helped by the tiny mike which had been built into the light fitting.

'How long have you been in Istanbul?'

'Do you know Paula Karsovina?'

'How much was dinner at Hilton last 21 February?'

'Did you sell any jade to the Greeks?'

'How much money did Gedik pay you to help?'

'When did you last see Chou En-Lai?'

'Is Khruschev planning war against the capitalist world?'

'Did you have a good holiday last year?'

'Where are your children?'

'What is anti-matter?'

'When will China have an atomic weapon?'

'Where were you born?'

'Have you made a will?'

'Who is your best friend in Turkey?'

'What is your real job?'

'How would you like to die?'

'Do you know Mao?'

'Do you believe in Communism?'

'Who is the best spy you know?'

'What do you know of the American Pilot Francis Powers?'

'Will China go to war with Russia?'

'Have you been in Paris?'

'What is going to happen to Israel?'

'Why is Russia removing her key men from China?'

'Who is Raul Castro?'

'Have you read any of Pearl Buck's books?'

'What is happening in the Belgian Congo?'

'Will you fly back to China?'

'Have you a mistress in Turkey?'

108

'What are the Russians going to do with Rhodes?'
'Do you know Paula Stoicheva?'
'How much money are you paid to be a spy?'
'Have you visited America?'
'Has your wife a lover?'
'Have you ever killed a man?'
'Who was Namik Gedik?'
'To whom did you give Turkey's secrets?'
'Why do you stay in Turkey?'
'What is your job in China?'

And as the list of apparently irrelevant questions was covered again, and again, and yet again, but always in a quiet, agreeable fashion, Turan noted the reactions of our victim, sometimes a twitching lip, sometimes a hostile stare or at other times a hurried walk up and down the tiny room.

It was an exhausting task for ourselves. What it must have been like for Sun I hate, even now, to think. The attack continued for four hours before we let up and it was only during the fourth that we began to see the possibility of results.

Later that day we studied Turan's notes. Sun had begun to show tension only on a few occasions but three questions in particular seemed to bother him.

'Will China soon have an atomic weapon?'
'Will China go to war with Russia?' and
'Why is Russia removing her key personnel from China?'

Two other questions had also provoked signs of minor irritation.

'What is happening in the Belgian Congo?' and
'What is anti-matter?'

At this stage I left Ankara for several days. My friends knew what they were doing and other work required my attention. Briefly they would continue the questioning routine, but whenever one of the 'sensitive' questions was posed a noise of some sort would also be made. A bell tinkled when he was asked about atomic weapons. A buzzer acted when asked about China going to war with Russia. A clicking sound was produced when asked about Soviet personnel being removed from the Chinese People's Republic: a hissing noise was linked to the Congo material and a whistle marked the question on anti-matter.

All this may sound childish and irrelevant to the reader but experience has shown that results can best be obtained by a complicated approach which creates a background of stress against a victim confused in his sense of time, and that if questions which provoke signs of tension can then be asked in association with a characteristic noise it is possible to build up a series of 'conditioned reflexes' due to the victim associating the noise with the question and exhibiting similar signs of stress either on hearing the sound alone or even when joined to another question which is perfectly harmless.

This technique may sound unduly bizarre but it has yielded good results and once a pitch of emotional tension has been created in the victim, first through systematically disorientating him in regard to his sense of time, and later in regard to the 'question-noise' reaction, it becomes possible further to produce a complete break-down of his resistance by the use of mild sleeping drugs and making pre-determined noises during the period when the victim is falling over to sleep. This has the effect of inducing dreams which can be predicted in advance through the inquisitor's knowledge of the 'noise-question' response, and when the victim ultimately does awaken he can further be frightened and confused by his inquisitor's knowledge of these dreams, a knowledge which seems to the victim at least, to be wholly incomprehensible.

The systematic infliction of tension created along these lines builds up in the end towards an emotional crisis the severity of which will depend to some extent upon the character resources of the victim. So also the time required to do this must depend upon the same factors, and we were all agreed that Sun would probably be a resistant subject. But we were equally agreed that he would break sooner or later and that he could then be exposed to the third stage of the investigation.

This phase calls for considerable skill on the part of the inquisitors. Having enclosed the victim for some time in a subdued unresponsive environment, having produced a sense of total personal disorientation of time and space, and having further conditioned him into believing that contact with previous life has been broken, that his tormentors know even his dreams and that

110

fear or irritation is now being produced in response to questions which seem in themselves to be harmless, the victim is encouraged to believe that he can, even then, build up a new type of life and that his inquisitors are sympathetic towards his problems.

He is encouraged to say anything which is on his mind, is given the opportunity to discuss his problems and is led to believe that the people around him will help him to solve them. Small doses of sedatives may then be introduced into his food in order to dull his inhibitions. Sleep is similarly introduced by that repetitive series of those noises which are known to produce tension or predictable types of dream, and with every awakening the victim is told the pattern of his reactions even during sleep.

When this is properly carried out it is not long before the victim feels an overwhelming desire to speak, to confess everything which it then seems has led to his present predicament. And again listeners are sympathetic until some significant indiscretion has been admitted, but at that point they pounce and their technique is instantly changed. The victim is not given a chance to recover his poise and he is grilled to the limit or until he has said enough to convict him of the offence of which he has been suspected.

His 'confession' is recorded. Inquisitors again alter their psychological approach. Better food is provided. The bed is made more comfortable. Lighting improves and the tape-recording is then played back to him at a time when he leasts expects it. This last shock is often enough to tip him into a frenzied desire to confess whatever may have been withheld and to break his final emotional resistance.

Where evil persons are concerned there is no need to do more at this stage. But for selected people it is also possible, using similar methods almost in reverse, or by applying other more recent techniques, to restore normality after a few weeks and indeed to enable the individual to return to a normal life in which his recent experiences are regarded as a strange dream closed off within the depths of a guilty subconsciousness.

'But,' said Ahmed when I left him on the third day, 'I do not think we shall bother about that stage where Sun is concerned and if our suspicions are correct.'

It was arranged that I would return a week later by which time we felt that he would be near breaking point, if, indeed, he had not already 'confessed'.

'But why,' asked Trudie when I told her of all that had been going on, 'do they waste so much time? If this man is so important could he not be persuaded to talk by some other means?'

'Torture?' I asked.

'It sounds horrible. But the position is terrible. Even torture might be justified.'

Others have asked the same question. Indeed even Turan felt that physical torture could be speedier in its results than this slow, painstaking breaking down of a man's mind. But practical experience is against the use of torture for any but the weakest types of individual, and they are the ones who are least likely to become involved in such a situation. Physical torture often reinforces resistance, the subject may even feel wholly detached from pain and not even the most horrible mutilations have succeeded in certain classical cases throughout history.

'No,' I added. 'This man Sun would not respond to death by a thousand cuts or matches between his toes. Ahmed's only chance is to persevere as he is doing.'

'Would the "truth drug" be any help?'

'It might,' I agreed, 'and indeed it may be used later on to double-check on anything he may say. But for the moment Ahmed is against it and he is dead shrewd. What he doesn't know about this racket isn't worth knowing.'

*   *   *

During these same days we were officially collecting material for our travel book on the New Turkey.* Our interests led us to an interview with ex-President Ismet Inonü, leader of the Republican Opposition, and to meetings with others of the country's business and political leaders including members of the Committee of National Unity. Former Ambassadors and leading socialites were blended with simple people in outlandish places to expose a broad picture of the struggling nation, its hopes and its aspirations for a long future.

* See *Doctor in Turkey* (Robert Hale, 1961).

But at no time did we find anyone prepared to discuss the former Minister of the Interior, his intentions or his suicide. Nor did any important public figure appear to suspect recent Soviet intentions. The Committee of National Unity was facing up to its duties capably and the people were behind the Army in everything which mattered. There was no obvious fear of world war and instead I sensed in high places a quiet conviction that all would soon be well in a bright future.

I even gave a broadcast from Radio Ankara: an unscripted talk describing my impressions of the New Turkey which was building and during which I tried to paint something of the fine impression which its new leaders had created in our minds.

Time passed swiftly and on 20 August I received a phone call from Turan. It was brief and to the point. 'Come back now.'

I was then in Central Anatolia but within ten hours had joined my friends in the silent house where Sun had been reduced to a gibbering bag of tensions.

12

The testing of Sun Yutan

'HE is ready to talk, I think,' said Ahmed, 'but we are going to leave him for an hour or two longer. Come and look.'

Together we went upstairs to the room in which we could see through the small one-way window into the cell below. Sun was a pathetic-looking object. His face was covered with an untidy growth of ten days' beard. His greying hair lacked lustre and had strayed untidily into ugly side-whiskers which curled around his tiny well-formed ears. He was pacing the cell like a caged lion, and like a caged wild creature his eyes darted restlessly from corner to corner, up and down, from side to side, alert, suspicious . . . and frightened. His pupils were maximally dilated and glinted abnormally. The whites were bleary with bloodshot strain and pussy discharge had gathered at the corners. His nostrils were finely drawn, lips sagging and wet with his tongue which constantly darted out and swept moisture around the blenched pink skin. His nails were bitten and he seemed to have lost weight.

He had been given a daily change of linen, and silk undergarments had been replaced by meshed cotton trunks and singlet.

'He has even given up washing for the last two days,' said Orhan Bey softly, 'and when we press the buzzer which reminds him about war with Russia he jumps like a cat. Look.'

Gently his finger pressed the small buzzer and in the same second the man below stopped dead. His eyes darted around the room and then his lips began to quiver and he burst into tears.

Orhan Bey lifted his finger from the instrument which was

jarring my own senses. 'Wait a moment,' he said, 'and I will show you something else.'

We smoked one quick Bafra cigarette and then he made a clicking noise with a tin device familiar to every lecturer. Click-clack. Click-clack. Click-clack.

The effect was extraordinary. The man slithered to his knees and slowly slunk along the angle of the wall to shelter in a corner where he crouched at bay with his teeth bared and hand raised as though to protect his face.

'This is horrible,' I whispered. 'Let's get it over with. Why not give him the chance to speak?'

Ahmed was watching with the academic interest of a scientist studying a laboratory experiment. 'Not yet,' he said. 'First we give him food.'

Turan was sent down with a glass of tea and some sweet biscuits. As the door opened the Chinaman trotted forward and almost grovelled at Turan's feet, pawing his arm and asking for help.

He was speaking a mixture of French and English plus something which we believed to be Chinese, and Turan was kind. He laid the tray of food on a small table which had now been added to the furnishings and tapped the man on the shoulder. 'Eat up,' he said in French. 'I shall come back soon and then we can have a talk.'

Sun drank his tea greedily. The biscuits were ignored and then he ran his fingers swiftly over his hair in a hopeless effort to comb it into some semblance of order.

'Now,' said Ahmed. 'Hoods on and let's go. I shall do the speaking.'

Our hoods were a nuisance as they became disagreeably warm after only a few minutes but Ahmed insisted that they were essential and that he did not propose to give his victim a chance to decide even the nationality of his captors.

When we opened the door Sun was sitting on the mattress, his eyes staring eagerly towards us, and he half rose to his feet as we entered. 'Sit down, John Sung from Shanghai,' said Ahmed pleasantly. 'How are you getting on?'

'There is a mistake,' said the Chinaman, also in English.

115

He was excited but trying to pull himself together. 'My name is Ma Yin. I am connected with President Ma Yin-ch'u of Peking University and I am not from Shanghai.'

'Why should we believe you? Men say you are John Sung. You lived in Shanghai and you swindled Western businessmen out of large sums of money selling imitations of antique porcelain. You sold forgeries of T'ang and Ming porcelain which were not worth a thousandth part of the price. You cost your customers over a million Chinese dollars. They would like to kill you.'

'I didn't. I swear I didn't. I know nothing about dishes.'

'Well, what are you doing in Turkey? Men say that you met American and Argentinian dealers in Ankara and Istanbul, that you made contracts with them to sell really valuable antique porcelain statues or other objects of art which you said you could smuggle out of the country through your influence with the Chinese Government and because it needed American dollars. But when you had taken their money your customers received only bad imitations.'

'I never talked to any Americans,' screamed Sun. 'I hate them. I even hate Turkey. I was only there because I had work to do.'

'Selling imitation antiques?' jeered Ahmed.

'No.' The man suddenly lowered his voice to a whisper and laid a hand on Ahmed's arm. His eyes were looking furtively round the room and his fingers were trembling. 'You mustn't tell anyone. Anyone at all. But I was in Turkey because I hate everything in the West. I am working for the Chinese People's Republic. I am trusted very much by them.'

'To sell porcelain?'

'No.' His fingers were quivering like a leaf. Even his voice had become unsteady and he was gulping mouthfuls of air. 'You've got to understand. It is important. I am the head of all Chinese agents in the Middle East. There may be a war soon and I have important duties. They trust me more than anyone else outside of China. No other man could do my job.'

'I'm not interested in spies,' said Ahmed. 'I want the money you stole from these Americans and Argentinians.'

The sensitive fingers were fumbling with Ahmed's sleeve and the man's eyes were desperate. 'You don't know what you are saying.

116

My country is already almost at war with Russia. We wanted to take them by surprise but Khruschev may have become suspicious and he has been recalling all his important men from my country. For all I know the war has already started.'

'War!' said Ahmed with contempt. 'Why should there be a war? What chance would China have against Russia? Does China have an atomic bomb? All China has is faked porcelain antiques. I don't believe you, John Sung from Shanghai.'

Sun looked at his tormentor with increasing desperation and for a moment spoke in his own language.

'Use English or French,' said Ahmed curtly.

The man hesitated and then spoke in torrents until at last Ahmed interrupted. 'You must tell me all that slowly and then perhaps I can believe you. First explain what you mean about China fighting Russia.'

'The Chinese People's Republic has gone through difficult times. Our Communist Party has tried to establish a full Communist State without having to make our people experience the misery of intervening socialism. We have done this and we have succeeded where the Soviet Union has failed. China,' he said, almost proudly, 'is the only Communist country in the world. The Russians are socialists running their country by State Capitalism.'

'And therefore you despise Russia,' said Ahmed. 'I can understand that.'

'We despise Russia because Khruschev and the men of the Central Committee of the U.S.S.R. Communist Party make claims which are not true. Khruschev is *not* the most important man in the world. It is not right that he should put himself across as spokesman for all so-called Communist countries. There is only one Communist State and its leader is Mao Tse-Tung.'

'Who is jealous of Khruschev's satellites, sputniks and bombs.'

'He is not jealous,' said Sun viciously. 'Mao is above jealousy. He was mentioned more than 1,000 times in the *New China News* between 21 May and 30 June, for example. When Khruschev visited Peking last October our own anthem "Red in the East" was played before the Soviet National Song. Can a man who enjoys popularity of that sort be jealous of a man like Khruschev?'

117

'Then is he afraid?' asked Ahmed seriously. 'I have heard it said that China threatens war against the whole world when her population reaches 900 millions, because with that number behind her to be atomized China would have a larger number of survivors than any other country and so be able to build a yellow global empire from the remains.'

'That is true,' said Sun seriously. 'But one of my own family, President Ma Yin-ch'u of Peking University, does not agree that we should let our population become so large. He wants birth control. He does not realize that man is the main source of wealth and that the more men a country has the more goods that country can produce. He is an enemy of the Chinese people and it is terrible to know that a member of one's own family is responsible for trying to put a brake on the official policy of our Chinese Communist Party.'

'And what has that got to do with you?' said Ahmed.

The man looked at him eagerly. 'I must work harder than ever to compensate for the disgrace to my family name.'

'But Mao Tse-Tung has accepted some things which President Ma has said. Birth control is now being encouraged in China.'

Sun's eyes flared with hate. 'And it is wrong. See here,' he said, pointing a finger within an inch of Ahmed's hood. 'My people are trying to learn what is the best way to do everything and our leaders study the lessons of other countries, but it is sometimes difficult to decide what is best and it is important to make no mistakes. Then again we still have Western spies in positions of importance, or deviationists who try to corrupt Marxist teaching. They also confuse matters and President Ma is one of them. He is a foolish theorist. But unfortunately some men are listening to him. Fortunately he is old and must die soon. When he dies the nonsense he teaches will be forgotten.'

'And what about this war with Russia that you spoke about? So far as I know it has not yet broken out.'

Sun eyed him suspiciously. 'Is that true?'

'It is true,' said Ahmed.

'It is difficult to believe. Mao Tse-Tung was prepared to start war against the U.S.S.R. during early September of this year. I have lost count of days but it must be September by now.'

118

'Why did Mao wish to fight the Soviet Union?'

Sun's reply was long and complicated but after an hour or more of questioning the argument became clear. War with Russia had become inevitable from the Chinese point of view and for many reasons.

Personal hatreds and rivalries at top level could now be resolved only through battle. Mao hated Khruschev, despised him for socialist deviationism and was jealous of the position which he claimed as spokesman for world Communism.

Soviet possession of formidable nuclear weapons had made it difficult for China to take positive action but now she realized that her own nuclear weapons lay in the relatively distant future and that in all probability she would never 'catch up' with the Soviet Union in this field. Disadvantageous, therefore, although her position might be, it could only become increasingly disadvantageous with the passage of time and if war was to come nothing could be gained by further delay. It must be fought now or not at all.

Expert assessment believed that China could fight a conventional type of war against Russia without fear of nuclear reprisals. This at first seemed to be a rash statement, but Sun's arguments might well have proved valid in the event. Broadly speaking, China did not think that Russia could take the risk of using any nuclear-type weapon without rousing world opinion through fear of 'fall-out'. It was also an undoubted fact that if global war did spring from what had been intended as an Asian domestic conflict the capitalist nations would support China, America would be obliged to support Peking and forget about Formosa, Britain and France likewise would be on the side of Mao against Khruschev and the technical potential represented by these forces when joined to Chinese man-power would make China's victory certain.

In the aftermath of such a global war China reckoned that she would emerge second only to America and that thereafter world spheres of influence would resolve into two vast sections, Australasia, all of Asia and most of Eastern Europe being controlled from Peking, with the American continent and Western Europe ruled by American dollars, and a vast uncommitted continent

119

of neutral Africa remaining to make its choice between the two titans.

Needless to say China believed that Africa's choice would be in their favour, that thereafter Western Europe could be plucked like a ripe plum and that the American continent might then, for practical purposes, be ignored for a century at least: that after such an outcome Communism would inevitably advance across the oceans and in due course absorb a decaying capitalist system which had lost its world markets and was no longer self-supporting.

If, on the other hand, the war against Russia did remain relatively localized, if thermo-nuclear weapons were not used and if the great powers did not become involved, China had absolute confidence in her own ability to win. She expected thereafter to absorb all that was possible of even European Russia, tolerate the liberation of the satellites for a generation at least, establish a live and let live 'temporary' arrangement with the capitalist free world and concentrate on developing her own potential until, at a later date, she was fit to seize the remainder of the globe. And after victory in such a 'conventional' war she would still emerge as second world power. Formosa would cease to exist and America would be forced to accept the new situation whether she liked it or not.

'What about anti-matter?' asked Ahmed.

Again Sun spoke at length but his torrent of words boiled down to two simple facts.

China had heard that the U.S.S.R. had a new weapon which had to do with anti-matter but he believed that it was only some development of a hydrogen bomb and not particularly mysterious.

'And why have the Russians been removing their important advisers from China during recent weeks?' asked Ahmed cautiously.

Sun began to settle down. His manner was less disturbed and his nervousness less obvious. 'Khruschev has been planning his own war. He wants everyone who matters to return from China to safe bases. And it was important for us to start our war first. To take him by surprise.'

'Do you think he knew what Mao was planning?'

Sun shook his head. 'It is impossible to say. But already we have been almost at war in the Congo.'

'I do not understand,' said Ahmed. 'Tell me more about the Congo.'

The Congo story, of course, is so complicated that probably no one fully understands all that was going on during 1960 and Sun's contribution did little to simplify matters. In short, however, he claimed that Soviet agents had organized early political discontent and had manœuvred affairs to ensure that the white population was forced to flee the country. Thereafter Russia had attempted to force a puppet government upon the people under the nominal control of Patrice Lumumba. When Chinese agents discovered how matters were developing they attempted to organize opposition from outlying provinces and to establish an opposition party capable of overthrowing Lumumba but acceptable to the United Nations.

Sun had only recently returned from Leopoldville himself and after his brief fact-finding mission had felt well pleased at the possibilities which lay ahead. China believed that Russia wished to use the Congo as a base in her own global strategy and that for that reason alone it was essential to obstruct her tactics.

'And now tell me about Israel,' said Ahmed. 'Did your men discover what Russia hoped to do in that field?'

The Chinaman nodded his head vigorously. 'Russia meant to drop some sort of weapon on Jerusalem and wipe out a city which is symbolic of Western civilization.'

'How was that going to be done?'

'By dropping a short-range missile from a Turkish base.'

'Did Russia expect to occupy Turkey as well?'

'Yes. They had an arrangement with some man to start a revolution and take over things for use as a Soviet base.'

'Which man?'

'I never discovered his name.'

'Who told you this?'

'I knew a Soviet agent in Ankara.'

'Tell me about this agent.'

Sun looked at us helplessly. 'There is so much to tell. I do not like women agents and this was a woman but she is an exciting woman. She appeals even to me. I knew that she worked for the U.S.S.R. and sometimes I think she knew that I worked for China but we pretended to forget about that and we satisfied each other.'

'Did she tell you anything important?'

'If she had told me anything I would not have believed her.'

'How, then, did you find out?'

'As they say in English I put two and two together. I also watched her very carefully. When she was drink taken she was also sometimes a little indiscreet and tried to tease me by saying things with double meanings.'

'What was her name?'

'Paula Karsovina. But she may have had another name.'

'How did you meet?'

'She said that she was a commercial traveller from a Balkan firm which wished to import silk from Shantung for important people.'

'Did you believe her?'

'I did at first.'

'What happened to make you stop believing her?'

'My people in China investigated her background as a matter of routine. They could not discover any Paula Karsovina and they believed that the business she represented was only a "front" run by Russian security agents.'

'Another question. Do you know Raul Castro?'

'Yes. He visited both Moscow and Peking several years ago. He has been a Communist sympathizer for a long time but he is not a party member so far as I know.'

'Who is behind him?'

'Dr. Rodriguez is Cuba's leading Communist and the most valuable man in the Cuban Party. He is the editor of the paper *Hoy* and Raul Castro does what Rodriguez tells him.'

'Is Fidel Castro a Communist?'

'No. He is a stupid man with only one virtue. He is a brave soldier and enjoys a fight. His stupidity and bravery showed when he attacked Moncada with only a hundred men. He proved that he was a good soldier in the guerrilla wars which followed some time later.'

'So he is simply the tool of Rodriguez?'

'And of his brother Raul.'

'So they will influence him to set up a Communist state in the West Indies?'

'Probably. But Russia is backing him and Khruschev will get all he wants out of him. Russia thinks he will be needed until war starts this autumn. But if we attack first he will never be used at all.'

'What about Abyssinia?'

'Russia has a base near Addis Ababa. She hopes to use it in her war against the capitalist world.'

At this stage Ahmed broke off abruptly. Tea and a meal of meat and egg-plant was served to his prisoner and we ourselves returned to a sitting-room to talk matters over.

Events which this book attempts to report are already complicated and it would serve neither the reader nor the cause of world freedom nor any interest in reading which the book may have if I had written an accurate account of Sun's dialogue with Ahmed. Their conversation did not flow so effortlessly as I have described and it was broken especially during the earlier stages by outbursts of tantrums, hysteria, pleading demands for liberty and all those pathetic manifestations of neurosis which the team had so painstakingly and successfully induced.

Almost every pont had to be probed again and again and the result would have been near chaos had not every word been recorded for later analysis. The account which I have given represents most of the edited version with which we were left after the essence had been transferred to another tape.

But even then Ahmed was not absolutely certain of his harvest. How much was fact, how much deduction, how much hearsay and how much imagination?

Later that day he decided to use a different approach and Sun was subjected to what some sensationalists have called 'the truth drug'.

Sodium pentothal given in small doses intravenously can establish a euphoric condition during which inhibitions are removed and answers are given to questions without subconscious assessment of their significance. On balance replies are probably truthful and evidence acquired by this means is now admitted in certain law courts throughout the world, even if not in Britain.

I never saw the man who gave it to Sun. I know only that during that evening Ahmed returned with a psychiatric expert and a list of prepared questions. Together they dealt with a prisoner exhausted by his earlier ordeals and only too glad to co-operate.

On the following afternoon I was given the result during our last conference together before we left for southern Anatolia and later returned by ship to Istanbul.

Everything which mattered had been confirmed and a few points of detail and other links in the chain had been discovered. The summer of 1960 must now be remembered as that period in human history when plots and counter-plots, coincidence of ambition by major powers and even coincidence in tactical approach reached a pitch of drama never before known.

In general, China had been preparing for war against Russia, hoping for a localized conventional-type conflict out of which she would have emerged as victor and as second world power, but prepared for nuclear attack if necessary, believing that she must then be supported by the capitalist world and that Russian defeat would still be inevitable, thus leaving China still a second world power.

But her plans had been disturbed by the unearthing of evidence of Soviet intent to attack the Free World from bases in Abyssinia, the Congo, Cuba, Turkey and probably in South-East Asia.

China had therefore attempted to forestall the U.S.S.R. by opposing her in the Congo and in any other place open to her. Sun believed that China's strategy in the Congo would prove successful and that parallel situations—even if less dramatic and publicized—were under control in Laos and Cambodia.

The Turkish problem had been solved for China by the Turkish Army and loyal students creating their own revolution. But if this had not happened China would have offered assistance to the Democrat régime immediately there was evidence of any uprising sponsored by Russia.

(It was a fascinating coincidence to discover that not only had two revolts been planned in Turkey itself but that each of the two leading Communist countries had also been making their own individual preparations for war, one against the whole world, the other against its alleged partner.)

But China had seen no reason to interfere with the Soviet intention to destroy Jerusalem unless it clashed with her own interests and I was delighted to find that matters in Turkey still continued to tie up with the broad pattern of facts and clues disclosed in Europe, that Hans's prisoner Spaak had been correct in believing that Russia had intended a demonstration against Israel.

The Castro fragment had also been confirmed and only two knots remained to unravel in detail. Where did Rhodes come into things and was anti-matter, in fact, the new Soviet weapon?

I left Ahmed and my other friends to return to the south with Trudie. It would have been tactless to inquire the fate of Sun Yutan. The man was a dangerous and dedicated Chinese Communist spy. He would have shown no mercy towards any Western agent captured on his own territory. Whether or not Ahmed would continue the brain-washing to that distant theoretical conclusion which might enable him to return a changed man into normal life was pointless speculation. Ahmed is a realist. Sun had said several times that he hated Turkey. His sympathy with Marxian Communism had been made clear. I shall be surprised if we see him again.

*   *   *

After such an interlude it was almost an imperative to return to Anatolia for rest and to enjoy for a little that serenity which envelops only the Valley of the Fairy Chimneys* before rendezvous-ing once again in Istanbul.

* *Doctor in Turkey*

125

13

Return to Istanbul

WE met Yildiz once more in the Park Hotel. She was offended that she had not been allowed to follow up what, after all, had been her own discovery and was still temperamental.

'I found all the clues which led Turan to Gedik's house and if it had not been for me recognizing that Roumanian hatchet-man we would not have unearthed these pictures or any of the documents which have made everyone so excited. And it was I and I alone who proved that Paula Karsovina was friendly with both Namik Gedik and the Chinese man. I even discovered Sun's address and then after all that work I am treated as though I was an unreliable "teenager".'

'But everything was decided by Ahmed,' I said helplessly. 'Turan and Orhan Bey had nothing to do with arranging who could follow up the Sun story.'

'They forget that Turkish women are emancipated,' said Yildiz viciously. 'And I am very annoyed about all this.'

'Then why don't you speak to Ahmed? It is unfair to be cross with Trudie and myself.'

'Ahmed!' she spat. 'Ahmed! Who is Ahmed? You have been sworn to secrecy. Even Trudie does not know him. Only Turan, who works for our security police, knows who he is. Orhan Bey has also been silenced and Turan has been very hurtful.'

I could see her point of view. Turan had proved to be the most important member of our little company. None of us had at first realized how deeply he had become involved in underground activities against the Democrats. He had passed himself off even to his intimates as an ordinary student with no especial political feelings above the average . . . and since most students were anti-Democrat he could afford to use that platform and still be considered normal. But after the revolt he had increasingly shown more and more knowledge of how to use information. He was never at a loss to know to whom he must go for help or with news, and when Yildiz had given him Sun Yutan's address in Istanbul he had reported at once to his Chief.

Ahmed had been satisfied with his work and had agreed that he could see it through to the end. Orhan Bey had been accepted because his reliability had been proven on several occasions during recent months and because his quietly reserved manner appealed to Ahmed's department. I myself had been sworn in partly because of Turan's recommendation but chiefly because I was known to be strongly pro-Turkish and working conscientiously to make the Turkish scene more comprehensible to the West. My record had been strung together by Ahmed's staff and they had accepted me as a 'brother'.

Turan had first introduced me to his Chief over dinner one evening and I had believed him to be an ordinary university lecturer. Our conversation had covered many subjects but in retrospect I now realize that I had been tactfully and efficiently grilled. A few days later Turan had invited me to his home where Ahmed was again amongst the guests and again we had argued the trend of world events.

On the following morning Turan saw me once more and told me that I could join him in certain specialized work on behalf of the Turkish people provided I would swear an oath of secrecy.

The invitation sounded dramatic but even then I did not associate it with Ahmed. When I agreed, Turan and another man then produced copies of the Koran and Bible respectively and I swore an oath of allegiance to the cause of their organization, undertaking to observe secrecy in all matters which might arise from contact with it.*

Once the oaths had been taken on the holy books Ahmed joined us and explained his own position as Director of a specialized department of counter-espionage. We shook hands

* I have been allowed to use material as described in this report.

and thereafter my activities to some extent at least were at the mercy of his orders.

When Sun was arrested Ahmed was generous and knowing my own interest in anti-matter allowed me to take part in the investigation.

I have now been allowed to describe these events only because names and places alike have been effectively disguised and because it is realized that the story is of international importance. But I have not been released from part of my oath and could say little even at that time which would satisfy Yildiz.

'You can at least tell me what happened,' she continued. 'Sun was *my* discovery and I have a right to know if he is important.'

'He is important,' I agreed. That at least was not a breach of secrecy.

'Did you discover more about anti-matter?'

'A little.'

'Or about Gedik?'

'Not really.'

'Or about Castro?'

'A little.'

'And Rhodes?' There was a glint in her eye as she spoke.

'Nothing,' I replied.

'Well I have,' she said triumphantly. 'And I am not going to let you know anything about it until you open up and give me all your news.'

But that, of course, was impossible.

'Then you can keep right on guessing,' she said.

'One point only,' I protested. 'If you have discovered anything which really matters to the world in general you simply must pass it on to someone. Did you tell the Embassies?'

'No comment,' she grinned.

'Or send it to the United Nations?'

'No comment. You tell me then I'll tell you.'

Yildiz is a good friend. She is a nice girl and I admire her tremendously. But she is very feminine and continued to be provocative. She is no fool, however, and I did know for sure that if her discovery was important she would at least have passed it on to the Americans and British.

Conversation then switched to other things but as the afternoon drifted past she showed no signs of relenting and in the end we said good-bye for another year.

'If there is another year,' she said slowly. 'The news is terrible.'

'Won't you let me know what you have discovered?'

'No,' she said. 'In spite of your good intentions you are simply an amateur. You are very obstinate and you haven't told me a thing about that Chinaman. I am just getting my own back.'

The word amateur rankled. Probably because it was true. 'Well, if every amateur tried to do so much for Turkey your country would be quite fortunate,' I said sourly. 'To leave us like this is unkind.'

She smiled wickedly. 'No Turk is unkind to his friends. I told Trudie everything which matters whilst you were collecting mail, telephoning and writing postcards. She will tell you in her own good time.'

'Shall we meet again in this world, Yildiz?' I asked. It seems a dramatic question when considered in retrospect, but on that lovely summer day above the Bosphorus it had a great deal of point indeed. We all felt lonely and were all a little afraid.

'I think so,' she said. 'There are straws in the wind which make me believe that the West is wakening up.'

'That there will be no war?'

She hesitated and then gripped my hand. 'If there is a war and if we all die at least we know that we shall meet again in Heaven. We have done our bit to help Light against the powers of Darkness and my Crescent and your Cross together will succeed. But if we die, we shall die knowing that the future will be brighter than the present, and that never again will the world be faced with such a threat to the dignity of human life. We shall meet either here by the Bosphorus or else by the silver lakes in Heaven.'

Swiftly I kissed her hand and she turned to Trudie. They looked at one another for a long second, embraced and separated with a brief word. '*Allaha ismarladik.*'

'Let's go back to the Blue Mosque,' said Trudie sadly, 'where our Turkish story began. Let's end this chapter there. I have quite a lot to tell you.'

The great building was silent when we entered and together we

sat under the spreading dome revelling in the numinous atmosphere which builds up within the place when tourists have gone
and when a fading sunlight gilds the carpets and marble with the
golden light of liquid honey.

'First my own news,' I said. 'There was a letter from Hans. He
has returned from South America and has been visiting Greece
and Italy. He knows that we are on the *Samsun*'s passenger list
for 2 September and asks us to see him in Naples on the 5th.'

'Everything seems to point to trouble in the near future,' said
Trudie. 'It is almost as though everyone was gathering for the last
act. Should we not fly home and collect the boys? I would be
happier if we were all back in Dunira. They might be safer on our
Perthshire hills.'

'No,' I said. 'This is not an ordinary war. This is one of these
strange metaphysical cataclysms which seem to hit the world
from time to time and I don't imagine we shall be safer in any one
place than another.'

'Meaning if your name is on it that's that?'

'More or less. I am becoming a fatalist so far as this is concerned. Man is no more master of the ship. Indeed Man has been
so busy making holes in the hull of his blasted ship that a force
considerably greater than Man will be needed to plug them all up.'

'So you want to follow our programme through to the end?'

'Correct. It is a lovely sail from Istanbul to Marseilles. I like
crossing the Ægean. Athens is quite nice and the trip round the
Peloponnese is marvellous. I love the Straits of Messina and with
a bit of luck Stromboli will be looking like an overgrown firework.'

'If what Yildiz said is correct,' whispered Trudie, 'much of the
Ægean may shortly look like an overgrown firework.'

'Why?'

'She says that Russia is considering dropping a hydrogen bomb
or something on Rhodes as part of her world attack.'

'Who told her?'

'Whilst you were busy in Ankara and when we were running
around Central Anatolia the Turkish Army switched on a top
security routine throughout the Eastern Provinces. With American
help they laid on a drill capable of shooting down even a fly if it
had crossed the frontier from Russia.'

130

'And did they get any flies?'

'Yildiz says they got two. One pilot was captured alive. He was arrogant and threatened disaster to anyone who harmed him. He hinted that Russia had a big surprise up her sleeve and that when Turkey found what was happening on her doorstep she would be begging the Soviet Union to help her.'

'What has that to do with Rhodes?'

'The man became frightened after a few days when he discovered that N.A.T.O. or the Turks were going to transfer him to some prison fortress in the south-west. He didn't like that at all and said enough to make them believe that he found the south-west dangerous. Rhodes lies just off south-west Asia Minor and Yildiz thinks that the two stories tie up.'

'Who told her what the Russian was thinking and how he felt?'

'One of her brothers is an air force "high-up".'

I remembered him well. We had dined together one evening and we found him impressive.

'And is that all?' I asked.

'Almost. But there is one other debatable point. The Americans believe that some big weapon went off accidentally somewhere near the Caspian or Van. It may have been in Russia but they say that houses felt the shock as far apart as Erzurum and Adana.'

This news did startle me. 'Adana?'

'Correct,' said Trudie. 'And it was in Adana that our car went out of control for a moment. You thought it was a freak gust of wind. Perhaps it was the blast.'

I remembered the incident well. On 26 August we had made a trip to Adana and had been approaching the city when quite suddenly the car had lurched heavily to the right and almost run into a shallow ditch beside the cotton fields. At the same time sheets of dust came wafting across the road and for a few moments the city was enveloped in a hazy cloud. I had felt a disagreeable buzzing in the ears and been vaguely unwell.

Adana is not far from the coast and quite often there is a breeze. A freak gust of wind from the Anatolian Plateau was less probable but still a possibility and beyond knowing that it had been rather frightening we had thought no more about it.

'When did Yildiz say that this explosion took place?'

131

'Twenty-sixth August,' said Trudie slowly, 'and if it did happen somewhere very high up between Van and Ararat it must have been some explosion indeed. The more I think about it the more frightened I become. Even these "Powers pictures" become more convincing . . . as if any more convincing was needed.'

'And is that all her news?'

'More or less. Only one other small point. There is a twenty-four-hour round-the-clock alert in all local N.A.T.O. bases and the Americans in Trabzon are on tiptoe. Frontier air patrols continue and at present the Batum murder beam is out of commission.'

'Meaning?'

'So far as Yildiz knows meaning nothing in particular. It is just one more of many facts. Sooner or later it may or may not be found significant.'

'What about Cemil? What has he been doing?' Cemil, the fourth of our student friends, had seen less of us than the others.

'He sends regards. He is working hard. His final examinations come along this year and he has left spying to other people.'

But I had one other fragment of news. Ahmed had given me a short list of names to be handed over to a contact in Piraeus. It detailed persons implicated by later questioning of Sun Yutan and was said to include the top Communist agents in Greece. He was sending them by two different routes and we were entrusted with one copy. My instructions were detailed and would, I believed, amuse Trudie when the time came.

We sailed from Istanbul on 2 September. The ship was quiet since Turks could no longer leave the country purely for holiday purposes until the Menderes Democrat Trials had been held. Most of the first-class passengers were either English or Spanish and a mixed bag of other Middle Eastern nationalities occupied the second and third-class quarters.

All in all there was a rather morose crowd on board, everyone seemed depressed and not even the Latin-American style orchestra could stimulate any atmosphere of gaiety.

We arrived at Piraeus on the forenoon of the following day and obeying instructions to the letter went ashore. Opposite our berth there were two newspaper and tobacconist kiosks not far from the

132

Olympic Tours Agency. First we walked past both of them and continued towards the series of souvenir shops which lend a little colour to the waterfront. At a certain point we examined some postcards of Athens and asked if there was a reproduction of that superb Head of Hygeia which seems to ourselves to be the ultimate gem of Athens' Archaeological Museum. The storekeeper said that he could let us have a good reproduction of the burial stele of Timaristo and Crito but that there was no Hygeia.

Still acting according to my instructions I then suggested that a good cast of the Head of the 'Blonde Euphebe' might be a suitable alternative.

The man then offered to telephone a dealer and suggested that I return in ten minutes.

We glanced at my wife's watch on the way out. It was eleven-seven a.m.

Slowly we sauntered along the street back towards the tobacconist kiosks and arrived at the most distant one at precisely eleven-seventeen . . . ten minutes to the second. As we lifted a copy of the *Daily Telegraph* a young man approached.

'Are you sailing on the *Jerusalem*?' he asked.

The S.S. *Jerusalem* was lying a few metres away from the *Samsun* and is the crack ship of ZIM (Israeli) shipping lines.

'Sorry,' I said. 'But can I help you?'

He laughed. 'I just wondered when she was due to sail.'

I drew out my wallet and looked at the shipping list. 'One minute. There is something about it down here.'

Trudie bought the *Telegraph* whilst I was studying the shipping schedule and slipped my envelope inside her folded paper.

'That's an idea,' said the youth in perfect Oxford English. 'Haven't read Peter Simple for days.'

'Take that one,' said Trudie, 'and I'll get another.'

In the same few seconds I told him when the *Jerusalem* was scheduled to leave, lifted the second *Telegraph* and walked off.

'That,' said Trudie, 'was a really corny effort. Who told you to go through such a rigmarole? Much simpler to have left your letter in the souvenir shop.'

I was feeling self-conscious about it myself but at least I had followed instructions. The young man had disappeared in the direction of the Customs shed . . . and the *Jerusalem*. No one had seemed to pay any attention to us. All seemed to be well. The message had been delivered.

'Perhaps after all,' said Trudie thoughtfully, 'we only feel self-conscious because we are amateurs.'

We passed the remainder of our Piraeus visit sipping coffee on the Athens side of the Ancient Theatre and looking down on the long bay which sweeps towards Sounion. Somehow the distant shimmer of the Parthenon was vaguely reassuring, a sign of permanence in a world which seemed to be preparing for ceremonial *hari-kiri*.

We sailed after a three-hour stay but the ship continued depressing and even Latin-American music became irritating after a few hours of dancing on the deck in the evening. Somehow it reminded one of Castro and of Cuba.

On the following day a heavy, sultry humidity hung over everything and we arrived late at Messina, but even there the lights seemed less brilliant and there was a sparkle of activity only for a few moments when the violinist played 'O Sole Mio'.

Stromboli, however, was the greatest disappointment of all.

We passed to the east of the little island and saw not even the glow of a distant cigarette. The volcano was dead as a dodo. Stromboli is my favourite Mediterranean island and I love to watch in the darkness when she puffs clouds of white-hot ash into the heavens. There is a sort of playfully effortless ease about it all which can be enchanting. Stromboli seems to be almost a toy volcano, a traveller's sample of wares found only at the centre of the earth, and I missed her mischievous firework display.

Trudie was even more disappointed but she was also superstitious in these days and chose to regard it as an omen. 'Perhaps it means that there will be no more fireworks,' she said.

'Or,' I corrected dryly, 'it may simply be the lull before the storm.'

Next morning we berthed in Naples and went straight to the Hotel Excelsior where Hans was waiting for us on a veranda café lounge.

134

14

Last fragments of the jigsaw

HANS was looking well. He had lost weight, acquired a tan and seemed unusually alert. He was smoking his usual clay pipe and we had a great deal to say. Since we had only three hours in which to say it we did not waste time.

'How about Spaak and Bormann?' I asked.

He grinned. 'Our clues led us to a man called Walter Figel but Bormann has disappeared.'

In parenthesis it should be explained to a generation new since Hitler's War that Martin Bormann was one of the younger businessmen who was primarily responsible for Hitler's rising to power. He became one of the top favourites in the Nazi Party and was with Hitler in his Berlin bunker almost to the end.

Shortly before his suicide with Eva Braun, Hitler drew up three copies of his own will. One was given to Bormann. The second was removed by a brave German woman called Hanna Reitsch who landed her small aircraft at the Chancellery right beside an opening into the bunker, and, despite almost direct fire from Soviet forces, succeeded in getting away. But Bormann was less fortunate when he attempted escape through the wrecked city and he was last seen running up a street which was being heavily bombed by low-flying aircraft. Buildings appeared to be falling around him and he was listed as killed in action.

I have been unable to discover what happened to the third copy of this famous will and I believed until recently that Bormann must have perished, that only Fräulein Reitsch had succeeded in reaching safety. Clues unearthed by those Israelis who captured

Eichmann, however, plus other evidence offered by Spaak, suggested that Bormann might, after all, have escaped.

'What do you think?' I asked Hans.

He shrugged his shoulders. 'Your guess is as good as mine. But Spaak's main value has been the dope he spilled about Soviet hush-hush armaments and his hunch that Israel would get the works.'

'Would you care to hear my own news?' I asked.

'I surely would. You must've dug something up during recent weeks and every little helps.'

I covered the story in detail and ended on a high note. 'War seems to be inevitable.'

'What dates have been given?'

'Seventeenth to twenty-seventh September.'

'That all ties up with my own notions but first let's go over everything again.'

For over an hour he covered the summer, our Turkish trip and especially the evidence of Sun Yutan, the Powers documents and events leading to Gedik's suicide. And then he relaxed. 'All will be well . . . even if the next few weeks are still a shade dicey.'

'And your own story?' I suggested. 'How much can you tell us?'

He grinned. 'There is a deal to tell and I'm not too sure right now how much is top secret. But we'll take a chance.

'Briefly you can take it that Soviet strategy will be to attempt destruction of the Free World in the near future by using outlying bases as deep freezes for her own most valuable men, women, documents, art treasures, and general top-grade personnel whilst the Motherland accepts whatever may be coming to her in the way of reprisals from surviving Western combat elements.

'Sun Yutan was dead right that Mr. K. was going to use foreign bases in his campaign. But not for offensive purposes. No, sir. Mr. K. was going to pump everything that mattered from Russia into them and then bank on the capitalist world not off-loading any nuclear warheads against the poor innocent populations of these places. In short, Russian treasure has to be protected by coal-black mammies and their curly-headed babies because Mr. K. stakes everything on the West being too darned sentimental to hurt them.

136

'And when the West has shot its bolt he will start rebuilding from scratch knowing that China can't do a darned thing to stop him.'

'Can you tell us any more?'

'Sure. And we'll start at the beginning. My South American trip was a dead loss in some respects since all present paths pointing to Bormann are dead ends, but I left Spaak there to work out his own salvation and then pointed north for Cuba.

'American agents had proof that thousands of tons of Soviet weapons have been dumped there since mid-June of this year and Raul Castro is a known Communist. Fidel has been losing popularity with every right-minded Cuban and it seemed to most of us that Mr. K. was going to give him a boost. We didn't rightly know where Fidel figured in the world picture but it seemed he was darned important to the Kremlin boys and that alone justified my trip.

'The country was swarming with Iron Curtain businessmen . . . but strangely enough there were few Chinese . . . and a police state has been set up along the usual lines.

'Now since police states rule by terror they shouldn't kick if we fight them using the same weapons. So we pulled in three or four of Raul Castro's men one night after a surprise attack by some of our guerrilla forces from the hills above Havana and we gave them the works.' He smiled apologetically. 'Forgive me. I have been with Americans for some weeks and picked up the language. But anyhow they talked and they talked good. By the time our boys had finished with them we figured Castro was cooking something big with Mr. K. and that it was even possible he hoped to use Cuba as a Soviet base from which Russia might occupy the States at leisure.'

'In fact,' I added, 'use it as he would have done Turkey.'

'Exactly. The question thus arose as to how Mr. K. could quietly walk into the United States without Uncle Sam doing something about it and that point has also been examined with some care by my own people in West Germany. Spaak the Jew also gave us some pointers and it seemed to us all that everything hinged on Soviet use of some good old secret weapon until it gradually also became apparent that Uncle Sam wasn't the only guy due for the high jump. Mr. K. was going nap on capturing the whole Goddam world.'

I had to laugh in spite of the seriousness of our talk. Hans was more American than the Americans. Even his suit had a smart New England cut.

'That is very true,' he said. 'I was also in New England. I bought it there and it set me back nearly two hundred bucks. It is a very good suit. I left Cuba stuffed to the earholes with hunches and flew north to have a word with the F.B.I. and some United Nations security boys. These operators know their stuff and they tell me that at least 600 high-grade doctrinaire Communist officials now work inside the U.S.A. Most of them are spies but they hold down official appointments inside embassies, at the United Nations itself, in consulates or trades missions and indeed all over the place. Obviously one can do nothing much about many of them, but even so at least nineteen have been asked to leave the country. But another 900 listed individuals, both men and women, also work under these top bosses, thus giving a grand total of 1,500 active and identified Soviet agents right inside the States.'

'Doing what?' I asked.

'Spying,' said Hans briefly. 'Just spying. On everything. They corrupt and blackmail private individuals. They record factory and industrial output; they foment unofficial and official strikes just as they do in Britain and they survey strategically important areas under a front of fishing holidays and the like.

'The two guys you saw in Moscow a couple of years back, Mitchell and Martin, are two cases in point to illustrate how the Russians exploit human weaknesses. And where a Mitchell or a Martin has been discovered the chances are that scores remain undiscovered. Indeed they ratted and went officially "red" only because our boys were on to them, but God knows how long they have been working for Russia and although they have never been in the top class they know enough to hurt.

'But . . .' said Hans slowly and with a slight return to his normal pedantic manner, 'other people work for Russia who are not protected. Sometimes they are caught and we nailed two in early August.

'You know,' he smiled, 'it is a pleasure to work in America.

The Police and F.B.I. are realists. In Britain you are much too gentle with suspects. I like American methods. They are simple. They are direct. And they are effective. The small fry also talked. Maybe they didn't say much but their passports showed visits earlier in the year to Laos, Cambodia and New Guinea. They had also visited Turkey and Cuba. Officially they were free-lance journalists from Hungary, and that would make a cat laugh because free-lance news-boys don't exist anywhere in the Communist Empire.'

'What did they say?' I asked.

'They threatened to see us hang if we hurt them and said that they would be rescued by Mr. K. himself.'

'Just as the Russian pilot did in Turkey.'

'That is so. These captured Bolshie bums seemed pretty damned certain that they would soon be released. And that,' he added, was very interesting indeed. But the tremendous question still remained. What trick did old man K. have up his sleeve? What was the secret weapon?'

'Did you find out?'

'Not for a little while and not at that time. But I had ideas. And in New York I had other ideas which centred on that hide-out which the Soviet Embassy runs in the country. Officially it is a holiday or week-end home for V.I.P.s, but the F.B.I. told me that no V.I.P. had ever been inside the dump unless he was a blood-red Bolshie from Kremlin town. In mid-August there was a great deal of activity taking place around that dear old country home for tired Bolshie Bosses.'

'So you kept an eye on it?'

'That is very true. We eyed it from the air and photographed it with some very cute infra-red and electronic devices worked out by some of the world's most clever men. We found that in all probability there were also several recent deep shelters all over the grounds with escape hatches made to order. Then again we drove a few tunnels towards it and got busy with geiger counters, with the same cute little infra-red devices and various other mysteries, until we were pretty damned sure that they had laid on shelters which are intended to be bomb-proof against everything except the Californian earthquake.

K *   139

'And while we were doing all that we also kept tabs on supply deliveries. The boys who covered that assignment were particularly good and they figured that hundreds of very peculiar masks had been delivered there during recent weeks.'

'Gas masks?' I queried.

'Just very peculiar masks. But the Commies were also stocking up one helluva lot of tinned and bottled food and we reckoned they were preparing for a siege or something.'

'Nerve gases?' I suggested.

He nodded. 'Yessir. Nerve gases came to mind right away and my own department back home in Berlin felt that they could be delivered from a nicely orbiting satellite crossing the U.S.A. from somewhere out west.'

He carefully removed his glasses and then beamed with delight. 'And then we had the only real bit of luck of our whole investigation. Concrete proof that a hundred thousand similar type masks had been delivered from a Roumanian ship to Fidel Castro's team in Cuba. The agent who discovered this died next morning against a wall and his widow will draw Uncle Sam's war pension for the rest of her days, but before they nailed him he had phoned the story through to his pal in Havana. It reached us within twenty-four hours and the picture then began to make some sense. Gas was going to be used somewhere, somehow and some time.'

'But I figured that was only one part of the Soviet global plan and got mighty interested in the Far East. Knowing nothing about these parts myself I asked the Americans to give me an up-to-date appreciation of the situation, and, by way of cross-checking, my own people sent another. I also did some homework on old news files.'

'Make this simple,' I said. 'I am not so well up on South-East Asia either.'

'Right,' he said. 'Cambodia, Laos, Viet-nam and Japan are the keys which will sooner or later open the Far East to either Washington or Peking. During 1960 Communist elements have tended to get control in several countries. The Japs were suborned enough to keep Eisenhower out. Neutralists in Laos who would like to make it an Eastern Switzerland are also on the up and up . . . which suits Russia well enough so long as matters pan out

140

O.K. elsewhere. But for "elsewhere" spell Cambodia and northern Viet-nam. There the writing is on the wall and unless a miracle happens the Red Flag will soon swing above every pagoda from Saigon to Hanoi. By mid-1960 there wasn't enough Soviet control to make a base but there was enough opportunity to make trouble and Communism thrives like a weed on trouble. So the way I then looked at it was this:

'If Russian grand strategy had worked out according to schedule she would by mid-1960 have had firm bases in Cuba, the Congo, Abyssinia, Turkey, Afghanistan and South-East Asia upon which she could build any missile stations she cared to.

'As things are in August 1960 she has got firm bases only in Cuba, Abyssinia and Afghanistan. But she still hopes to punch a bit out of the Congo and she still, even now, has hopes of something in the Far East.

'With all that plus her submarines, missile sites from the Bering Sea to Bulgaria and an odd sputnik or two she is still betting on scooping the pool.'

'Using gas?'

'At first I thought so, and quite possibly delivered from some low-flying sputnik thing because that now seems to be technically possible and discharge could be controlled from ground bases.'

'Space men are not required?'

'No. Space men would have a sales value to the more simple uncommitted countries in a cold war. But they are not needed for sputniks in a hot war.'

'How about anti-matter?'

Hans looked at me thoughtfully. 'This has been your pet theory for some time. Before we say any more tell me what you *know*. Not what you deduce or think possible. Just facts.'

Boiled down to sheer basic facts there seemed really very little to go on. But I did my best.

'Khruschev has referred to weapons of unbelievable power. In my view he meant something much more deadly than hydrogen bombs. We all know that these can reach a pitch of destructive power hitherto unimagined. But now we *can* imagine. Therefore his new thing must be something even more deadly.

'Secondly, the photographs which are alleged to have been taken by Francis Powers's U.2 show that a small range of mountains has been removed by something and I don't think that a hydrogen weapon could do that.'

'Anything else?' asked Hans.

'No. Everything else is either guesswork or deduction.'

'Right,' he said grimly. 'Then here are facts which are neither guesswork nor deduction. You have told me enough to fill in the few gaps in my own picture. And we have been talking round the subject for long enough. World war is due to start between 17 and 27 September 1960. You got that one right.'

'In about twelve days,' whispered Trudie. 'Twelve days!'

'But if all goes well it will not start at all,' said Hans. 'So quit fretting about these boys of yours. And in any case you will be home a week before zero hour.'

'Don't be awkward, Hans,' I said. 'Make it snappy. What is the programme?'

'All summer,' he said, 'matters have been simmering in the Belgian Congo like a witch's brew of hate. China has been trying to counterblast every Soviet move and for weeks matters have been so complicated that not even Dag Hammarskjöld knows for sure what is really happening. But the struggle for power continues, and it will continue until someone throws the Russians out. For months they have been pumping men and materials, weapons and all sorts of scientific equipment into the heart of the jungle. They are already behind schedule and are racing like Hell to get everything ready by mid-September for an overwhelming demonstration of white man's scientific magic. This coon Lumumba is dangerous and he has friends in high places: some of them even in the United Nations itself. They will back him to the limit and if he has his way his Bolshie friends will direct a shot of their new weapon to rub out opposition provinces and any other hunk of country ol' man Patrice Lumumba thinks fit to name. Black Africa will go mad overnight. Ghanian occupying troops will wet their pants with funk and Black Africa will repay a few old scores. Whites will be slaughtered from Cape Town to Dakar, and from Durban to Entebbe. And in the middle of all this the Russians will sit tight on their own little island of security surrounded by Lumumba's picked men, plus fire-bombs, nerve gas and God knows what else. When it is all over they will walk out and quietly take over the whole of Coloured Africa from the Cape of Good Hope to the Sahara.'

'And how will that help them?'

'This is very complicated,' said Hans. 'But briefly it is a second string to their bow. Remember, though, that when they originally planned this campaign they had hoped to use the Congo for other purposes.'

'As a depot for their own man-power whilst the remainder of Russia got its load of nuclear weapons in reprisal from the West?'

'Exactly. Russia now realizes that she can never defeat the Free World in a hot war without paying a heavy price. But the price can be reduced if she uses outside bases in which men who matter can be kept safe for the all-important business of restoring life to the stricken Motherland.'

'And the Congo was intended to do just that?'

'Correct. The sequence of events was to have been quite simple.

'The Congo situation would be developed to leave a puppet Soviet Government in power and that should have been achieved by mid-June according to the official schedule.

'Turkey, of course, was to have been occupied by mid-July using a Gedik puppet government.'

'But China upset Soviet timing in the Congo and General Gursel completely disrupted the Turkish plot,' I suggested.

'Even so the Abyssinian enclave has been well prepared and well-equipped forces of all sorts have been flown into it for many weeks. Russia has had several years in which to get ready and few Western people know that it even exists. I believe that the explosion over Eastern Turkey was the *accidental* detonation of a hydrogen weapon at 70,000 feet or more whilst in transit from bases near the Aral Sea to Addis. Its course would lie across the southern end of the Caspian. It has been calculated that blast at such an altitude from that point could have reached south-east Turkey. It also affected much of Georgia and parts of northern Persia.

'Then again although Khruschev has been packing everything possible into the Addis Ababa area, selected items have also been pushed hard and fast into Cuba, and by way of encircling China he has established long-range missile sites around Lake Baikal and north of Alma-Ata.

'A fleet of Soviet vessels has already left for the South Pacific. Their rôle is to control a sputnik which is now laden with their new supposedly secret weapon. This thing will be sent into orbit on Friday, 16 September. When it is on course and orbiting at eighty miles altitude it will be "released" of its weapon at approximately Longitude 120°, Latitude 40° and if expert appreciation is correct a wedge will be punched out of the American continent from Canada's Slave Lake to the Rio Grande and from Vancouver Island to the Great Lakes. The Rockies will disappear and the Pacific will sweep across the continent in a tidal-wave which will stop only at the Appalachian Mountains.

'So much for that. But in Europe itself there was a plan to eliminate Rhodes, using a shot of the new weapon delivered from a Turkish base, and that is still possible, because delivery may still be attempted from a missile lobbed across Anatolia from near the Aral Sea where sites are already loaded. It is calculated that this neat little demonstration will be sufficient to subdue all opposition in Eastern Europe and Rhodes has been chosen because of its situation. Apparently it is considered possible to eliminate that island without producing any serious aftermath of tidal-waves or storm.

'But Western Europe, of course, is another kettle of fish and missiles suitable for the job have also been laid on to cover American bases in England, France, Germany and Spain. They will be loaded with the new weapon and that will be that. It is accepted at this point that surviving Western aircraft or any still in the air will retaliate and that various missiles may be launched against the U.S.S.R., but Mr. K. is not worrying overmuch about them either.

'And as you also discovered, the agnostic Kremlin killers decided at the same time to get rid of Jerusalem. A compact little 1945 vintage atomic weapon would do that and so remove a symbol of culture and civilization which is like a red rag to a bull. Jerusalem, even today, represents the Great God Jehovah and as such it is due to go before a new culture based on Satan can be built on earth.'

'So Spaak was right?'

'Yessir,' said Hans. 'That boy was dead right about Israel and he has passed on his ideas to everyone who matters. In some respects it made bigger headlines than anything else.'

'You make my blood run cold,' said Trudie slowly. 'How can you speak so offhandedly about these things?'

'Patience,' said Hans. 'Take it easy, lady. Relax and listen to the rest of my story. One other sphere of influence must be considered, the Far East. There the target is obvious. Formosa. Or Taiwan, as the Chinese prefer to call it. Rub out Formosa and mainland China will be happy. Mainland China will also then have to accept the reality of Russia's secret weapon and will be less likely to attempt war of any kind.

'Formosa's missiles will be delivered from submarines. It is felt that the mission may be suicidal but Russia is taking no chances on any transcontinental ballistic weapon going off course and landing on China itself. Avoid trouble in that quarter if possible seems to be the motto.

'But there is also the problem of American bases in Okinawa and elsewhere in the Far East. Okinawa also goes and will be eliminated by the same means as Formosa, the new weapons to be delivered from submarines.'

'And where will Khruschev be whilst all this is going on?' I asked.

Hans smiled. 'At sea. The United Nations meets for its fifteenth session on Tuesday, the twentieth of this month. Friend Khruschev knows that almost anything can happen when he starts this lot so he is going to travel to the States by ship. By a slow ship. By S.S. *Baltika*, in fact, and with him he will have his team-mates in crime, János Kádar of Hungary, Antonin Novotny of Czechoslovakia, Gheorghe Georghiu-Dej from Roumania, old man Gomulka from Poland and last but not least His Communist Excellency Todor Zhikov of Bulgaria.'

'What about his own people?'

'Your brother was the first to hint at this. You yourself got confirmatory evidence and I unearthed more from another source. Soviet strategy is to remove from the Motherland photostat records of every significant document, all her key technicians and personnel, all her top leaders and everything else which she judges necessary and then to accept whatever may be coming to her.

These together with a mass of armed forces are now being prepared for swift transfer to the Abyssinian base or to any other place where Khruschev thinks he can dump them during the dangerous critical period. He himself expects to land like a conquering hero in New York and to be the first Communist leader to step ashore in the defeated Western World. His glory will then be shared by the other Satellite leaders. Same idea as Hitler going for a drive through Paris when he captured it in 1940. People don't change much. Not even tyrants.'

'And do you seriously believe that this is possible?'

'It would have been possible if we had not got on to it.'

'We?'

'A few people like ourselves who work to try and keep the world clean for rogues to fight in.'

'What counter measures have been arranged?'

'Ah,' said Hans slowly. 'That is a difficult one to answer. But I know a little. A remarkable new American submarine which must be the most powerful thing afloat is already *en route* to the Far East, as are several specially appointed aircraft. It is expected that they will successfully cope, but I can tell you no more about that.

'Then again an American submarine will also follow the *Baltika* during the whole of her voyage and everyone feels that Khruschev will hesitate to attempt destruction of the Free World if he knows that he himself and his treasured stooges will perish in the same hour.

'By way of making certain about this one or two other offensive weapons will also be hovering about in the offing, and really I don't see what the enemy can do about it.

'Cape Canaveral will be appropriately loaded to the hilt with enough to blow up Castro and all his family if anything happens, and that is always another safeguard even although we know that K. doesn't give a dime for either of them, neither Raul nor Fidel.

'Enough aircraft will also be flying in various other parts of the world to drop a tidy load of hydrogen eggs on selected targets and carefully timed "leakage" of information will ensure that Mr. K. finds this out after he has been at sea for a few days. It will be brought to his notice that the capitalist world won't be so

146

sentimentally mealy-mouthed about all these coal-black mammies and curly-headed babies after all and that if there is a good crimson Bolshie target it will be worth a nuclear weapon whether it be in Leopoldville, Addis, Kabul, Havana or East Berlin.'

'But you still don't know for sure how Khruschev proposes to use his new weapon. You don't even seem to be quite certain as to whether it will be anti-matter or nerve gas,' I said.

'You are quite wrong. We do know. He has two strings to his bow and his first hope is to punch out bits of territory here and there with anti-matter released from a trans-American sputnik or at other places from submarines and aircraft.

'But his second string is nerve gases. And we believe that if his first string don't make a big enough pop he'll switch on the nerve gases, using a similar technique on 27 September and at a time when he is dug into his week-end hidey-hole near New York City. I can just see him strolling the garden wearing his gas mask and laughing like hell when the clouds roll up Fifth Avenue. And under these circumstances he can still fly in troops from his various foreign bases to occupy the unconscious Free World before it has wakened up. They tell me that unconsciousness is complete for two days and that for at least a fortnight afterwards people are left weak, incapable of thinking straight, physically uncoordinated and emotionally confused. Think what these Kremlin hustlers could do with sixteen clear days of action against a helpless enemy. It would be a piece of cake.'

'It would take a tremendous number of occupying troops to hold down America and Western Europe,' I protested.

'Not so,' said Hans. 'It only means taking over key airports, naval and air bases, barracks, radio stations and missile sites. They are all known, thanks to the work of these 1,500 spies I mentioned earlier. It has been calculated to a "t" how many troops will be required to achieve this and remember that ninety-nine per cent of the "enemy" are expected to be unconscious. Moreover, recently developed nerve-gas guns and anti-matter short-range weapons make it possible for small numbers of effectively equipped men to do as they please with vast numbers of prisoners. The same applies to Western Europe, but so far as Australasia is concerned Russia believes that the whole area can be controlled by intercontinental ballistic missiles whose warheads are loaded with anti-matter.'

'How many would be required? The stuff can't be all that plentiful,' I argued.

'You forget the psychological effect of what will already have happened,' said Hans. 'Mr. K. is relying on Australasia being scared sick. He calculates that only one anti-matter missile would be required. At the first sign of resistance it would be released against the Central Desert and the Aussies would find themselves with a lake as big as the Black Sea. After that they wouldn't kick any more.'

'What would be the end-point?'

'Chaos,' said Hans. 'For some time at least there would be sheer chaos. But it would be a sort of controlled chaos because here and there in the middle of it Mr. K.'s outlying missile sites would still menace the entire globe.

'No one would dare to lift a finger throughout all of Asia.

'The Africans would be petrified with fear and at worst there would only be massacres of whites in the inland cities, perhaps some old-fashioned tribal warfare and amongst the Moslem peoples a swift decision to play ball.

'India would be able to do sweet damn all.

'Eastern Europe likewise would have to accept the new *status quo*, and throughout Russia itself there would still be plenty of smaller cities and villages where there was no damage. It would only call for a bit of organizing to clear up the mess and the whole project would have been perfectly feasible.'

'Given surprise,' I added.

'And if the West had listened to all its cry-babies, kicked the Yanks out of England or Germany, given up nuclear research and quit spying.'

'Why then are you so certain that Russia will be defeated?' asked Trudie.

'Because,' said Hans, 'the Americans are a very great people, because they have weapons which are almost as good as anti-matter and because they have brave men prepared to use them: because they have the courage of their convictions, in spite of their peculiar ties and strange manners, because to them freedom is still important and because they have inherited our European culture and Christian civilization: because Western Europe is still led by men of genius who know what may happen and who can contribute their little bit of effort to drop a spanner in the Soviet works: because your Mr. Macmillan is one dead shrewd guy in spite of his haw-haw manner and aristocratic self-assurance: because men like myself and women like Hanna work and die to keep the Free World safe from Communist tyranny, and because, in short, we are better men with better weapons and finer ideals behind the weapons than all the Bolshie bums from Kremlin town put together.'

There was a long silence, and then: 'How did you find all that out?' I asked.

Hans was busy polishing his glasses, surprised, I think, by his own unexpected outburst of emotion. 'Part of it is deduction. But you worried from one angle, your brother from another, I and various other people have all been chewing on it from others. When our findings are pooled the set-up becomes obvious. Or should I say the tactical approach becomes comprehensible.'

'But you have no positive proof that all this is so?'

'Shall I say that the Free World has arranged its defence on the supposition that all I have said is true?'

'But you have no highly placed agent in Russia with access to Khruschev's top secrets.'

There was another long silence. 'There may be. There probably is.'

'But you can't talk about it?'

'That is so.'

'But you can talk about what you discovered yourself, and when all our clues unearthed from Turkey, Argentine, Cuba, Berlin and so forth are strung together you still believe that these are Khruschev's intentions.'

'That is so. Without any inside gen from Moscow's Communist Party Headquarters we would still believe that Mr. K.'s been thinking pretty closely along these lines.'

'Why has there been no leak to the newspapers?'

He smiled. 'Be your age, boy. This is top-level stuff. Only a very few men or women know what we know and you are one of

them only because you had the savvy, the intuition, to spot something suspicious when Serov mentioned anti-matter to the
Americans in 1958.'

'Not intuition,' said Trudie. 'Call it a suspicious nature.'

'Call it anything you like, ma'am. The fact remains that your
husband reacted where most other guys would have done nothing.'

'But what did I do?'

Hans looked at me with a mischievous twinkle in his eyes and
broke into loud laughter. 'As a spy you are a dead loss. As a
trouble stirrer you are in the first rank. You poured out your heart
to me. You told Mr. Bernard Newman who is one very smart
fellow indeed. You got in big with Turan in Istanbul who is quite
the smartest chap of his size and weight in the game. You blew
your top to Gedik and scared him stiff. You poured out your ideas
to several other well-placed Turkish friends who know how to
string two and two together as well as the next guy. You went
about quietly blabbing to everyone for two years, and brother
Alistair got the latest dope every morning over coffee. You didn't
miss a trick and you worried at anti-matter like a dog with a
bone. You deserved all that Turan and Ahmed did for you and it
would have been a darned shame if they hadn't let you in on Sun's
grilling.'

'Trudie did more than myself.'

'Sure,' said Hans. 'She kept her mouth shut and she lost weight
wondering if you would get into trouble.'

'So I'm just a blundering amateur.' Yildiz's word had returned
once more to sting.

'Not "just". Not "blundering". Not even "amateur",' he
smiled. 'You are unique. A sort of special model which broke all
the rules and got away with it.'

Not altogether away with it, I thought. Stoicheva and Sofia were
still nightmares which I tried to forget.

'I can't say much about that,' said Hans slowly. 'It is one of
these bizarre episodes which shouldn't happen but which occasionally do. But they knew you by that time as well as I did and
they probably guessed you might be more valuable alive than
dead. I am sure they would keep an eye on you for some time
afterwards.'

'You know nothing more about Paula Stoicheva?'

'Only that there are several female Balkan or Soviet agents called Paula. Probably a security device intended to confuse.'

'And there is still no news from Hanna?'

'None.'

His voice discouraged further questions.

'So we can now only wait and see what happens,' said Trudie.

He nodded briefly. 'Already things are beginning to warm up and if I am correct the fifteenth session of United Nations will open with more top-level statesmen gathered together round a conference table than has ever been seen before in world history . . . even at Versailles. There will be only one important absentee.'

'China?'

'China. And for years China may continue to be the great enigma. But her population can expand to a thousand million if it likes and thanks be to God we now ought to have weapons capable of controlling even her bloody-minded maniacal leaders.'

'And will Francis Powers serve his ten years' sentence?'

'If the next American President has the guts of a louse he will refuse to discuss anything with Khruschev until Powers has been liberated and returned to his family. Their motto ought to be let the dead past be buried. As a a gesture of goodwill Khruschev should recognize the tactical stalemate by releasing Powers and in return Uncle Sam could very well afford to let loose several agents at present watching television in various state penitentiaries. After that the next President could get down to brass tacks and start talking about how to live together under the shadow of Polaris missiles, anti-matter guns, hydrogen warheads, sputniks loaded with nerve gases and men on the moon. Some world, isn't it?'

Our time was up and he walked back with us to the ship. Naples was dusty as ever and Vesuvius still withdrawn behind a heat haze. The gang-plank was still down but we had cut it fine. Next stop Marseilles.

We drove to Rotterdam in a day and a half, collected our children and returned to Scotland on 11 September.

'Six days to go,' said Trudie.

151

15

The last round-up

SEVENTEENTH September 1960 was zero hour for the Soviet High Command and Mr. Khruschev sailed for New York on board the Soviet ship *Baltika* with every reason to believe that he could still rely upon an element of surprise to ensure ninety per cent global success, but believing that even if there had been some 'leakage' both his master-strokes could hardly fail, and that within ten days he would be not only master of the world but—for the first time in his life—master of the Kremlin with all which that symbolized.

In the event it seems that the last-minute up-to-date appreciation to reach him before sailing was reassuring.

Turkey, he was told, could be forgotten. A demonstration against both Rhodes and Jerusalem was feasible without Turkish bases. The Soviet Union had sufficient 'space to manœuvre' in other areas to ensure that forces could swiftly be transferred from there to any necessary theatre of operations and that rehabilitation teams could similarly be returned to the Mother Country with minimal delay as and when necessary.

Units built up in Abyssinia were considered adequate to seize key points throughout Africa and designated areas of the American continent and were given two weeks to complete the 're-disposition of forces'.

Civilian, scientific and other technological personnel were already massing in the Congo. The numbers were not yet large because the personal intervention of Mr. Hammarskjöld, Dr. Bunche and other United Nations officials had interrupted preparations for the local reception of reinforcements. Even so

Patrice Lumumba, the Congolese Premier, was co-operating well with his Soviet advisers and there was no reason to anticipate complete failure. The 'demonstration' planned for 17 September would take place, and African reaction would be maximal. Mr. Lumumba guaranteed that this reaction would be controlled and diverted along prepared lines to ensure that by 19 September Soviet–Congo forces would jointly control all airfields. Diversionist, reactionary and capitalist elements would have been 'removed' and the theatre opened up for the smooth reception of all necessary equipment and forces.

Missile sites along the Black Sea coast, in the Karelian isthmus of Finland, by Lake Baikal and around the Aral Sea were waiting for the count-down. Targets throughout Western Europe, the Middle East, Southern Asia, Australasia and the Pacific Islands had been pin-pointed for elimination and all major Western submarine, air, naval and land-force targets would be 'neutralized' within one hour of firing.

Movements in Afghanistan had been impeded by local opposition elements which would later be 'removed' but sufficient progress had been gained by Soviet forces to ensure free use of two bases in that theatre through which the subjugation of India–Pakistan could be guaranteed. Occupying forces would thereafter be flown in from depots already stocked with men and materials throughout the Turanian Plain.*

Attacks due to be mounted against Formosa and Okinawa from Soviet nuclear or other submarines would proceed as arranged and all commanders had been fully briefed. These islands would have 'ceased to exist' by 10.00 hours Central European time, 17 September.

Three hundred and fifty Soviet submarines would be submerged in their allocated positions by 20.00 hours Central European time. These vessels would carry selected key personnel for specialized tasks ashore following upon destruction of their targets in synchronous conjunction with all other forces.

Co-operation from Raul Castro in Cuba had made it possible to establish important depots throughout that island theatre 'on the

* A plain extending north-east from the southern end of the Caspian Sea towards the Kirgiz Steppe.

very doorstep of the enemy' and expert assessment believed that neither Cuba nor the south-eastern American States would be involved, even indirectly, by the destruction of 'extensive land masses' on the western sea-board of the American continent.

Ballistic missiles would destroy Cape Canaveral in the same synchronized operation devised to eliminate all other previously listed targets in other theatres.

All existing Soviet aircraft would be airborne at maximal altitude five minutes before zero hour. These aircraft would each carry pre-determined passengers or other loads and would adhere rigidly to courses and positions given at final briefings before take-off.

Three 'space vehicles' had been prepared and mounted for action. One, carrying a 'weapon of elimination', would be released on 17 September as part of the globally synchronized plan for the annihilation of all enemy targets. Soviet ships were at present preparing to rendezvous in the Pacific Ocean as part of the co-ordinated task between ground (or sea) and space weapon, and in order to control and direct the satellite towards release of its destructive content at the selected target point over the American continent.

The Soviet High Command had accepted as a 'theoretical possibility' the fact that Western Intelligence might become informed of Soviet global grand strategy. It further accepted that counter-measures might be devised by an alert enemy. Should this prove to be the case the 'machinery of political negotiation would be brought into action' and zero hour would be advanced by ten days to Tuesday, 27 September, by which time the enemy would have been 'lulled into a sense of false security'.

Given this premise an 'alternative operation' would be launched and the remaining two 'space vehicles' would then be put into orbits of election. Soviet vessels on duty at their Pacific stations would continue to control these weapons until they were released of their 'paralysing vapours' over target areas in synchronous operation with 'weapons of elimination' as previously scheduled under the original plan (but excluding the 17 September space-vehicle).

In the event of 'Operation Elimination' (the first project) being successful, Soviet and 'allied' air forces would proceed with the return of Soviet 'forces of rehabilitation' to the U.S.S.R. immediately it became clear that no further retaliation was possible from the defeated enemy.

In the event of 'Operation Paralysis' being forced upon the High Command, Soviet and 'allied' air forces would engage in the joint task of occupying pre-determined points throughout enemy continents and at the same time returning 'forces of rehabilitation' to the U.S.S.R. when enemy reprisal attacks had ceased. Selected Soviet and 'allied' personnel throughout enemy continents would wear special anti-paralysis gas masks throughout this operation and for seven days thereafter, or alternatively until advised that it was safe to discard them.

Since these 'paralysing vapours' did not kill, but merely rendered victims incapable of positive action for approximately two weeks, it was not necessary to risk leakage of essential plans through the indiscriminate protection of Soviet personnel. Nor did 'drift' of 'vapours' at high altitudes become a significant danger to Soviet citizens living in Russia or elsewhere. At worst only a small proportion could be affected by them and then only temporarily.

More important was the risk to life through 'Western' reprisal or counter-attack.

There would be an inevitable lag of ten to fifteen minutes after launching all Soviet ballistic or other missiles before the enemy could take action. A further ten to fifteen minutes would elapse before enemy missiles could be delivered against Soviet territory. There would, therefore, be a period of one half-hour during which Soviet Civil Defence teams would prepare for action and all comrades would have the opportunity to take cover.

Preliminary 'news flashes' at three and two hours beforehand would warn the people of an important announcement. This announcement would then be made within one minute of zero hour and these preliminary warnings would have ensured nation-wide listening. The people would then be ordered to take instant shelter. Coal and other mines, quarries, deep ditches and the like would be available for their use. They would be ordered to carry with them as much food as possible and allowed fifteen minutes to reach a position of relative safety.

In the same hour a memorandum would be delivered to the Governments of China, Japan, Australia, New Zealand, Turkey, Iran, Greece, the United Arab Republic and all South American states informing them of the nature and purpose of current developments.* Peking would be further advised that steps had been taken to protect the Soviet Union against attack from any source and by any means.

* * *

It is not surprising that the *Baltika*'s august passenger list sailed conscious of the fact that they were making history and confident of success.

Until 16 September all was apparently well. A stream of radio messages continued optimistic and none imagined that its complex code could be broken down in under many months of labour. Communications therefore poured across the North Atlantic in an unending series of frank dispatches each rivalling the other in sinister import.

The first body blow was delivered on the evening of 16 September only a few hours before the 'count-down' for attack.

It was a signal from the Czech Ambassador in Leopoldville to Prague and it was followed almost in the same minute by one from Soviet Ambassador Yakovlev, also in Leopoldville, to Moscow.

President Kasavubu of the Congo had ordered all Soviet personnel out of the country.

Patrice Lumumba, Premier of the Congo, had overnight lost power to Colonel Mobutu.

On 23 August Lumumba had been rebuffed by the Security Council for his general policies. On 25 August he had again been criticized by the thirteen 'little African states' and been privately warned to modify his approach to almost every problem. Thereafter he had thrown in his lot with the Russians. Fleets of Soviet Ilyushin planes had then flown in hundreds of Soviet 'experts' to Stanleyville during the following two weeks and hundreds more had massed around Leopoldville. Activity had been directed

---

* It is interesting to note that one Soviet Ambassador delivered his memorandum in advance of time through some clerical error which may yet cost him dear. Possession of this note gave, for the first time, an authoritative picture of Soviet strategy.

almost exclusively towards preparing a major 'demonstration' of Russian technical power somewhere in the outlying provinces. And now, at the last moment (almost), a virtually unknown, smiling, bespectacled warrior had arranged an overnight reversal of power. Lumumba was left helpless and President Kasavubu gave the entire Soviet establishment until midday on 17 September to leave the country. His armed forces surrounded each Embassy and every Communist ambassador was escorted under guard to the airport for a noon take-off.

Hungarian, Czech, Polish and even Chinese journalists, scientists, alleged medical teams and all technicians were ejected with a slick efficiency which made striking contrast to the blood-soaked chaos which had hallmarked the Lumumba administration.

And Colonel Mobutu, consciously or unconsciously, stopped not only further Congo tragedy but played a major part in disrupting Soviet plans for world domination.

The Congo was most important to Soviet success. Aircraft due to make the long passage from the Addis base to the Americas were to refuel in Leopoldville where immense reservoirs of high-octane fuel had been built up in advance. On that count alone the Congo was desirable because in no other part of the North African continent could the Russians be certain of adequate fuel or service under the circumstances which they visualized.

But other events were also developing in the Far East and at the moment of writing it is not possible to report with assurance what really happened.

I can only say that I discussed anti-matter with Bernard Newman some months before he made an important Far Eastern journey to India, Pakistan and Formosa. He lived for some time with Chiang Kai-Shek and lost no opportunity to assess the local situation.

Formosa, of course, is a major bastion of American authority and Hans has now collected evidence suggesting that at least one American (query) Polaris-carrying submarine left America in mid-August for an unknown destination. This submarine returned in late September having previously been posted as 'missing'.

But mysterious events also took place on remote Ritter Island, a tiny place not far from New Guinea and strategically poised to dominate not only the entire Indonesian Archipelago but also much of Australasia and, of course, even China. A superstitious aura has always enfolded this place and even white men have recently been reluctant to land, knowing, as they do, that others have died mysteriously soon after reaching the shore. Ritter Island was ideally sited to be a missile base and there is reason to believe that the Russians did, in fact, develop it for that purpose. On 17 September 1960 the island 'exploded'.

It was described as 'Terror Island' by the *Sunday Express* on the following day and the explosion was attributed to volcanic eruption. In the light of other considerations it seems probable that at least one of Russia's 'weapons of elimination' (anti-matter) developed some major technical defect *before* zero hour and released its force locally. There were no survivors.

The latest news from Hans suggests that the American submarine also sank various Soviet craft on 16 September. Certainly there is reason to believe that local American action did eliminate opposition. It is also probable that Ritter Island blew up because of some technical defect in the (query) anti-matter weapon prepared there to menace China, Formosa, Okinawa or Australia . . . the point has not so far been made clear and probably never will.

But it should be remembered that Soviet strategy did envisage a need to have a suitable 'weapon of elimination' prepared against Australia in the event of opposition from that lusty little continent.

But most important of all, the 17 September Soviet sputnik failed to go into orbit. This weapon was due to be launched some time before zero hour, and indeed zero hour was based upon the time when it would cross Longitude 120°, Latitude 40°. The weapon failed for causes at present unknown to myself or to my friends. Probably the second stage mis-fired but the war-head certainly landed in north-western Mongolia quite near to its launching site at Lake Baikal and not far from Dzhargalantu.

Men who know of these events have wondered if, once again, Providence chose to interfere in the affairs of man. And while it is true that Soviet scientists may have proved their skill in controlling technically advanced space machines of one sort or another it is equally true that they still have failures. It is providential that the 17 September failure was one of them.

News of these disasters began to reach *Baltika* early on 17 September and by the same date news that big events were impending had reached several other world leaders. It is probable that few of them know even today what exactly happened but enough was suspected to make them realize by 18 September that the fifteenth session of the United Nations must become the most important of all.

King Hussein of Jordan, Presidents Sukarno of Indonesia, Nasser of Egypt, Tito of Yugoslavia; everyone excepting the Prime Minister of Great Britain, President Nehru of India and a few others swiftly announced their own intentions to represent their countries.

Mr. Nehru later joined the pilgrimage saying that 'events had obliged him to go'.

Mr. Macmillan said nothing at first and was reviled by the Press for lack of leadership, for indecision, or alternatively for trespassing upon the authority of his Foreign Secretary if he went at all.

But Mr. Macmillan must have known the story and I believe that he remained in England until he was confident that Soviet strategy had been finally and irrevocably checkmated.

Because there still remained the question of 'the other bomb'.

Operation 'Paralysis' remained for consideration and counteraction.

Two consignments of gas masks had been off-loaded from Eastern European cargo ships at Matanzas near Havana between mid-June and early August 1960, and American intelligence suspected delivery of another batch through Santiago. Maximal effort had been made to secure even one specimen for examination but Raul Castro's security arrangements had been effective. There was also doubt as to which particular type of nerve gas might have been developed by the Russians, and as there were several possibilities, each of which required special treatment, it had not been possible to develop a comprehensive 'broad-spectrum' protective respirator.

Attack by nerve gases delivered from two sputniks or 'space-machines', and reinforced by ballistic missiles carrying anti-matter or some other 'force of elimination', remained, therefore, a strong possibility unless decisive counter-measures were immediately brought to bear upon all angles of the situation.

American reaction was swift.

First of all the *Baltika* was shadowed by American submarines and remained at all times within striking distance of aircraft either land-based or mounted upon carriers.

The presence of this unwelcome escort was made known to Khruschev on 17 September through radio messages which proved that the Soviet code had been broken.

Experts in acrostics, ciphers and the like are no longer required to break a code and the Soviet High Command, together with its technical and security advisers, had forgotten that any code could always, eventually, be deciphered given enough time, but that modern use of specially prepared 'electronic brains' can do in an hour work for which a team of experts would formerly have required many months or even years.

The machine which broke the Soviet code is, according to Hans, the most advanced thing of its kind in the world. He is also proud that several German mathematicians and cryptographers were associated with its development.

Scientists are not supposed to use their skill to ventilate their sense of humour but these men would not have been human if they had not wanted to enjoy a laugh at Soviet expense. I am told that their first message to the *Baltika* read:

Surprise. Surprise. Surprise. All has been discovered. Uncle Sam.

Other more formal messages followed within the hour using the same Soviet code and advising Khruschev of counter measures planned in the event of aggression. They are said to have included:

The use of cobalt bombs against the entire Soviet Union in a calculated weight sufficient not only to destroy life in all forms for more than eleven years, but to prevent use of Soviet territory for a further eleven and until the cobalt isotope had been exhausted.

The destruction of listed targets by Polaris weapons, only

then coming into production, but already sufficiently numerous to threaten the Soviet Union from any point on the world's oceans. Mr. Khruschev was further given to understand that since these vessels could remain at sea and submerge for very long periods reprisals would be continued throughout even one whole year . . . or even more under special circumstances.

Finally it was made clear to the *Baltika* that no nerve gas or indeed any other weapon of offence could be used against the Free World without the Communist leaders themselves instantly becoming the target for attack either by the 'neutron' bomb—which has lately been revived for possible use under selected circumstances—or should it be impossible to attack using the 'neutron' bomb, then to blast the area in which they might have taken shelter with either a cobalt or hydrogen weapon *even at the expense of American or other lives.*

This last threat was one of the last which any passenger aboard the *Baltika* could have expected, believing as they did that Washington would be less ruthless than the Kremlin when it came to demanding sacrifices from its own people.

These messages, together with reports of catastrophe in the Far East, throughout the Congo, and joined to knowledge of the 17 September 'space-machine' in Russia, were delivered to Mr. Khruschev by secretaries terrified for their lives by even his first reactions to the Congo situation . . . which, in itself, need not have been absolutely fatal to the final outcome given total success in all other theatres.

Khruschev has revealed himself to the world as a man of many moods and his capacity for camouflage is of long standing. It is interesting, today, to read expert assessment of the Soviet political scene during the years before Stalin's death when every political commentator was attempting to predict his successor. I have read almost all of these books and in none was Mr. Khruschev mentioned even as a remote possibility.

Study of news files covering the battles for power within the Kremlin after Stalin's death also fails to reveal any evidence that he was regarded as a serious rival to Malenkov or indeed to anyone else.

And yet it was he who eventually emerged as a smiling father figure of a man from the welter of blood and dust which surrounded the exit of Beria, Molotov and Malenkov. And his early use of Mr. Bulganin as partner was a flawless example of his ability to confuse.

Mr. K. and Mr. B. became the butt of every second world comedian whilst they flew by jet plane all over the globe and into almost every capital city. Almost were they like a couple of slapstick comedians, and the ruse succeeded. The world was charmed by the new world dictators.

I saw Mr. Bulganin walking in the Kremlin gardens on the day of his official demotion. He did not appear to be worried. His face was as genial as ever. His pipe was drawing freely and he seemed happy only to walk amongst the rose-beds and sniff the young buds. Was this demotion, I wondered, or was it only the attitude of a man who had done his job well and was now off for a holiday? He knew himself to be a nonentity. He liked being a nonentity. In Russia even in these days it was safer to be a nonentity.

With his departure Mr. Khruschev began to show some of his other qualities. There was the genial grandpapa playing with children; the strict disciplinarian rebuking his juniors for failing to produce their 'norms'; there was the repentant sinner who had been misled by Stalin and who was determined to paint the Soviet Union with sunshine rather than with blood; there was the dedicated Marxian theorist arguing points of dogma with Peking; the peripatetic ambassador alternately threatening or promising, often misunderstood but praying on all sides for peace; and there was the psychopathic monster of Paris who, for the first time, terrified the Free World when he dropped the mask and showed something of that younger Khruschev who had walked with death throughout the Ukraine and played the part of Stalin's hatchet-man in the bad old days which so many liked to think had been forgotten.

But on board the *Baltika* on 17 September 1960 there was another Khruschev who had not so far been revealed to the world, a man white with fury, tense with passion but controlled at first by a discipline which was even more frightening than his open rage.

Later, as the news worsened, his self-control became less and less until the day ended with a concentrated tirade of venom directed against America and Britain, against Gursel, and Mobutu, against Eisenhower and Francis Powers and against even those of his own people who had bungled the 'space-machine' launching, who had been taken unawares by American counter-attack in the Far East, and who had disrupted the detailed planning of experts even in Cuba, where knowledge of anti-paralysis gas masks had been exposed by American Intelligence and proven a useful pointer to Soviet intentions.

As he spoke he used every peasant analogy in a wide vocabulary to describe his hatred for the parade of unseen and unknown enemies who had made such a public fool of him, and his reaction to America's first 'Surprise' radio message scared even Kádar and Antonin Novotny who were with him at the time.

And then rage gave place to sheer panic. What would Peking say?

What would Marshal Malinovsky say?

What would that . . . Malenkov say? Or Molotov? Or Zhukov who had claimed to know all the answers?

*   *   *

The full story has not yet been pieced together: only enough to know that on 17 September 1960 Nikita Khruschev learned that his bid for world power had failed: that it had failed completely: that it could not again be attempted and that the best he could hope for would be a return to a 'cold war' of attrition for the loyalties of countries at present uncommitted.

But even then he guessed that many of these smaller states would learn enough to be scared off for another generation.

Before the *Baltika* berthed in New York Harbour on Monday, 19 September, evidence as to how these lesser states were reacting had already reached him. Almost every world potentate was *en route* for the General Assembly and rumours were already suggesting that the uncommitted Afro-Asian countries would be lined up against him.

It is also known that he panicked. And that he panicked not only because Soviet strategy had been completely disrupted but because he knew that as leader he would be required to shoulder full

163

responsibility in the eyes of those men who still remained in Moscow and amongst whom he still had many enemies.

It is said that he panicked because he also knew that a day of reckoning must come with China and it is believed that above all he panicked because he feared for his own future life and liberty. For a moment he remembered how Beria had fallen upon the cement floor with a bullet crashing against the base of his brain and remembered that even in Russia it has been said that those who live by the sword will perish by the sword. For a moment he relived the last moments of Stalin when the old man threatened to destroy Russian Jewry and Kaganovitch had stepped forward threatening him with death if he persisted in his policy: he saw again the twisted face, the cry, the fall, a dying hypertensive Stalin moaning on the carpeted floor of his Kremlin study: and then that sudden exchange of glances between all those members of the Politburo who were present, recognition that this was their moment of truth, that now they must act or perhaps themselves die: and he saw once more those clutching fingers which reached out from all sides and strangled the last breath from Stalin's gurgling throat.

And it is said that he saw the dead Stalin lying side by side with the dead Beria, their bloody heads and twisted faces leering at him from among the ghosts of the scores of thousands who had perished at his own command throughout all of the Ukraine. His mutterings sounded like the ravings of a maniac and his threats terrified even those few privileged persons who found courage enough to stay beside him.

And he also panicked because he saw himself lying amongst all the other bodies and leading a rolling, piling, range of corpses which swept across the ocean to the Pripet marshes, and beyond to the endless steppe-lands of Eurasia. Corpses dead from starvation, by shootings, by hangings and by the sword or bayonet. Corpses of intellectuals and simple peasants, noblemen and kulaks, men and women, children and old folk alike, all destroyed to build a classless Paradise which was as remote today as it had been even in the days when he had bashed out the brains of cats against the walls of his mother's cottage before the First World War. And as his bemused brain watched the glazed eyes of unknown millions leering at him from their putrefying range of death he saw too those countless millions more who had been doomed to join them from the Americas and Europe, from Southern Asia and Formosa, from Australia and Okinawa, Rhodes, Africa and Jerusalem, all laughing and jeering as they pointed mocking fingers at the fat little man who had planned their end.

But the name which he muttered more than most was Mobutu. And the name which he cursed more than most was Eisenhower. The name which he pitied most of all was his own.

* * *

His doctors had two days in which to sedate him and his own vigorous obstinacy also reasserted itself, as it had always done when confronted with danger. He had less than two days in which to adjust himself to his altered situation but when he finally walked ashore on American soil he was prepared to face the toughest battle of his career.

He knew that hot war had probably been banished for ever by the tempo of scientific advance on either side . . . American and Russian. But he knew also that at United Nations he would be fighting a personal war on several unseen fronts and that his future would depend not only upon the showing which he put up but also upon how he prepared against his return to the Soviet Union.

It is a matter of recent history that his campaign was directed first against Mr. Dag Hammarskjöld, Secretary-General of the United Nations, and that the General Assembly supported Mr. Hammarskjöld's actions in the Congo by seventy votes to nil with eleven abstentions.

His subsidiary efforts to enlist the sympathetic support of Afro-Asians were as unsuccessful as his campaign to remove the Secretary-General.

At best he emerged after weeks of battle knowing that the cold war must continue and that much of it would be fought in Africa where protestations by Guinea, Ghana, Tunisia and Egypt would be less dogmatic when confronted with cast-iron offers of Soviet aid in the development of their countries, and knowing too that these, and possibly other countries which had voted against him

165

in the General Assembly might still be wooed and won by other means and in other places.

But he also learned that young African and other States are less naïve than he had suspected, and that where major issues of Big Power intervention are concerned they are likely to use the platforms of the United Nations for their own purposes and with at least as much skill as the Communist countries themselves had shown in the past.

But most of all he learned through endless 'behind the scenes' contacts that bluster would no longer be effective and that the Free World had ample resources whereby to defend herself against aggression from any quarter. He was also forced to accept that no power on earth could now attack without the certainty of itself being destroyed . . . even though using outside bases as a cold-storage bank for its more valuable human assets.

Soviet strategy had been cunning. It had also been sufficiently ruthless to have ensured success given ninety per cent surprise and successful preliminary preparation, but neither of these pre-requisites had been achieved.

From time to time however Mr. Khruschev hankered back to the impossible and early in the proceedings he threatened to give the world a demonstration of Soviet authority on Tuesday, 27 September. Moscow radio also announced that 27 September would be remembered as the outstanding day in human history.

But his two 'space-machines' never left the ground and by 27 September they had probably been rendered harmless. The day passed like any other, and with no more drama than most.

Mr. Macmillan finally left Britain to attend the General Assembly when it had become clear that all danger of world war had been removed. But he did not forget to warn America that Mr. Khruschev was *still* unpredictable and operating under very real pressures both from the Soviet peoples and from Communist China. He described the Soviet Premier as being in a 'touchy mood' . . . a superb example of understatement but on a par with his own speech on 29 September when he dealt with Mr. Khruschev as a kindly but experienced headmaster at a better-quality English public school will handle a recalcitrant pupil who refuses to improve his standards.

The British Prime Minister's speech was that of a man who not only holds all the best cards but knows it and knows also how best to use them. Perhaps most important of all he ended his speech on a note of willingness to forget the past, to banish recrimination and embark instead upon thoughtful negotiation of all outstanding problems.

His manner, more than that of any Western statesman, showed that he knew his team's strength and it speedily became evident that few of the smaller states would disagree with his assessment.

The effect upon Mr. Khruschev was deadly, and for the second time—but now in public—he came near to panic and was on the verge of one of those rages which only a few months earlier had terrified the world.

Now the world smiled, and when Mr. Khruschev became the central figure in a scene which reporters have described as 'one which the world leaders gathered here will never forget' he knew, and they sensed, that his sting had been removed.

Few of them knew how the miracle had been achieved. There were even those who preferred to remain ignorant. All realized that some subjects are too dangerous to discuss even with friends.

At the end Khruschev once more hankered back to his dreams of power and there were more flashes of wishful thinking but this time directed against Britain.

'If the United Nations want war, keep on provoking us and you will get it. That well-known English unsinkable aircraft carrier will *discontinue its existence on the first day*.'

He still could not forget his 'weapons of elimination' and the operative word is 'elimination'. For months the words 'annihilate', 'remove', 'eliminate' had become familiar parts of Soviet aggressive jargon. Now the clumsy phrase '*discontinue its existence*' was added to the list.

*   *   *

I discussed the situation with Hans for the last time just before completing this manuscript. Some months had elapsed since his American visit and he had lost his mannerisms. Once more his English was formal, and even ponderous.

'Our case has been proved,' he said. 'Part of what you have

167

written was reasonable deduction. Now we can confirm much. Rumours of Khruschev's arrest reached the world Press on 4 November. Other mysterious changes in the High Command had taken place during the previous fortnight. It is obvious that when he returned to Moscow—and this time by air—he returned to face strong criticism. But he lingered in America long enough to have his escape lines prepared and his own men hotted up for action.

'Malenkov and Zhukov moved just a shade too late. Reports that they had taken over and jailed Nikita were proven false by 6 November. But the fact remains that there was still one more struggle for power within the Kremlin and that once again the jovial little fat man came out on top.

'A few die-hards had been probably anxious to have it out now anyhow and damn the consequences. But Nikita is shrewd. Dead shrewd. And he has learned enough to know that hot war cannot pay.

'Then there is China. He has learned enough to convince even Peking that hot-war days are over. Think of it. On 5 November, only one day after he had been rumoured in jail, he meets the Chinese delegation to celebrate the forty-third anniversary of the Russian Revolution. Almost all the Chinese top brass was present, led by Liu Shao-Chi, Head of State and the highest ranking Chinese to visit Russia for three years.

'What mysterious events lay behind this fantastic meeting? A meeting in which Liu immediately upon arrival speaks openly about "the indestructible union of the *Socialist camp led by the Soviet people*".

'Think of it,' said Hans solemnly. 'Could any man alive who knew the facts in early September ever have imagined that the Chinese would, within six weeks, make it clear that they regarded Russia as leader in the East: that they included themselves, China, in the Socialist Soviet bloc, and that by implication they were renouncing their most treasured claim to distinction, that they were the only Communist country in existence and that they had reached Communism without any intervening condition of Socialism? For some people this may not sound very dramatic, but it is, believe me, the most important thing which has happened since 1946. China has now publicly accepted her position as Number Two Man in the Socialist–Communist bloc. She has further declared agreement that neither war nor revolution are now necessary to establish world domination and she will, in future, have to tone down her strictures against Soviet Revisionists.

'China's change of face is due to one thing only, her recognition that not even an expanded population of 900,000,000 will be able to survive attack by weapons at present owned by the Free World. It is a further recognition that Peking's only chance now lies in burying her differences with Russia and joining with the Kremlin in an all-out cold war based on trade and commerce against the Free World but fought in the back-yards of the world's backward, uncommitted nations.

'The next few years should bring immense advantages to all the have-nots from Haiti to Cambodia. But if the next American President can reduce taxation he will be a genius.'

There was a long, long silence whilst we brooded about the events of the previous two years, of Serov and Martin and Mitchell, of poor Hanna and the creature Stoicheva, of conspiratorial conversations in Istanbul's Blue Mosque and the ordeal of Sun Yutan.

'But you see,' said Hans slowly, 'I was perfectly right, Trudie. You did return to Dunira and to the boys. The next generation, and many generations to follow, will probably be perfectly safe. Americans know that somehow or other Ike has done it again and he is more popular than ever. Mr. Macmillan has enough up his sleeve to confound all the fellow-travellers in Britain who are making such fools of themselves within your British Labour Party, and given knowledge of the background to all recent events even Mr. Gaitskell should be able to stage a full return to power and emerge a greater man for his sufferings. And he deserves credit for the stand he has taken, a patriotic and realistic stand which rises high above party or self-interest. I don't know whether he knows the story or not, but he behaves as though he did and he too has earned his place in history.'

'Will the cold war continue?' asked Trudie.

'Sure. But so long as America produces a sufficiency of Polaris missiles and nuclear submarines, develops her neutron bomb for

Early in September 1960 Sir Anthony Eden gave the world his opinion that 'war was nearer than it ever had been since 1939'.

In August 1960 Sir Winston Churchill said that 'despite everything I feel in my bones that there will be no war, although in 1936 I felt in my bones that there would'. Once again the words of this great and wise man have been justified by the play of events.

For the first time in human history there is now reason to believe in a future in which world war has been eliminated as an instrument for solving any international problem whatsoever.